'If you are a creationist it is m[...]
time you finish reading this thou[...]
who is, like myself, a Darwinia[...]
the foundational Genesis narra[...]
Charles Foster explores why w[...]
fractured world but also propels us to a new and lyrical vision
of a world crafted by evolution, but permeated by meaning and
beauty, and ultimately to be made perfect. This is a book the
atheist Darwinists will loathe, but I'll bet anything they won't
have an answer.'

Professor Simon Conway Morris,
Department of Earth Sciences, University of Cambridge

'Charles Foster shows himself a true disciple of Darwin by
choosing the difficult option of defending reason against the
fundamentalism of both religion and atheism. He succeeds marvel-
lously. His book is fun to read and an important antidote to the
shrill hysteria about evolution from both extremes. Such unreason
ought to be rejected out of hand but still captivates many people.
Read *The Selfless Gene* and inwardly digest it.'

Sam Berry, Professor Emeritus of Genetics,
University College London

'Science and religion are frequently thought to be at odds.
However, in this book Charles Foster assesses the arguments of
creationists, intelligent design, Charles Darwin and Richard
Dawkins, and shows that there is no conflict between science
and the Bible if both are properly understood. The book is
written in a clear and lively style, and contains many fascinating
facts: I found it difficult to put down.'

Professor Colin Humphreys,
Professor of Materials Science and Director of Research,
University of Cambridge

The Selfless Gene

Living with God and Darwin

CHARLES FOSTER

HODDER

First published in Great Britain in 2009 by Hodder & Stoughton
An Hachette UK company

This paperback edition first published in 2010

1

A CIP catalogue record for this title is available from the British Library

ISBN 978 0 340 96441 5

Typeset in Monotype Sabon by Ellipsis Books Limited, Glasgow

Printed and bound in the UK by CPI Mackays, Chatham ME5 8TD

Hodder & Stoughton policy is to use papers that are natural, renewable
and recyclable products and made from wood grown in sustainable forests.
The logging and manufacturing processes are expected to conform to
the environmental regulations of the country of origin.

Hodder & Stoughton Ltd
338 Euston Road
London NW1 3BH

www.hodder.co.uk

A great deal of the universe does not need any explanation. Elephants, for instance. Once molecules have learnt to compete and to create other molecules in their own image, elephants, and things resembling elephants, will in due course be found roaming through the countryside ... Some of the things resembling elephants will be men ...

(Peter Atkins, *The Creation*
[San Francisco: Freeman, 1981], p. 3)

Then the LORD answered Job out of the whirlwind:
'Who is this that darkens counsel by words without knowledge?
... I will question you, and you shall declare to me.
Where were you when I laid the foundations of the earth?
Tell me, if you have understanding.'

(Job 38:1-4)

Contents

List of Illustrations

Acknowledgements

My debts are many and heavy. None of them can be discharged fully here, and only a few of them can even be mentioned.

I am neither a professional evolutionary biologist nor a professional theologian. I am a professional assessor of evidence, and have relied heavily on the biologists and theologians to tell me what I should be assessing.

Michael Lloyd's work on the problem of animal suffering fascinated and inspired me long before he became a friend. He read some of this manuscript in draft and made a number of important observations.

Professor Sam Berry and Dr Chris Thouless also read the manuscript, and steered me away from some dangerous biological rocks. Both are splendid, learned field biologists of whom Darwin would have been proud.

Professor Simon Conway Morris's comments on the draft manuscript were invaluable, and have saved me from some deep embarrassment.

I have found particularly useful the work of Leon Kass on the meaning of the Genesis account, Simon Conway Morris on convergence, Jeff Schloss on the evolution of altruism, and Ian Tattersall on human evolution. My gratitude to them is inadequately reflected in the endnotes.

Although he wouldn't put it this way, Andrew Powell taught me that the noblest destiny of a biological scientist is to be a naturalist, and that to lose sight of the whole animal in peering at its DNA is a catastrophic error. That was a crucial and repercussive lesson.

James Orr patiently put me right on the Greek.

Wendy Grisham, Katherine Venn and the team at Hodder have been tremendous. There are no more efficient, creative or downright congenial publishers.

As always, my long-suffering wife Mary and the children have been victims of my absence and my brooding. I am very grateful for their forbearance, but very sorry that it was necessary.

Preface

I wrote this book because I was angry and worried.

I was angry at the fundamentalist reductionism of Richard Dawkins and his enemies (yet crucial allies) the creationists. And I was worried that if the only explanation for the complexity, colour and variety of the natural world was the selfishness and struggle intrinsic to Darwinian natural selection, it was as immoral to enjoy a walk in the woods as it would be to watch a snuff movie or a piece of extreme sexual sadism.

Richard Dawkins, seen by the TV-watching and paperback-reading public as representing mainstream science, is on the extreme jack-booted right wing of evolutionary biology. Very few in the trade think that things are as simple as he thinks they are. Real biology bristles with fascinating caveats.

If few in the business agree with Dawkins, almost nobody thinks there is anything at all in any of the creationist contentions. It has been to the mutual benefit of these extreme factions to emphasise the divisions, and that is exactly what they have done. Contention is colourful: it draws congregations; it sells books. People love a fight. It is more fun than measured discourse.

In his 1860 debate with Huxley, Wilberforce tried to parody Darwinism into extinction. He famously failed. Since then, Christianity and Darwinism co-existed pretty happily – although with little real conversation – until the relatively recent rise of creationism, a movement that sprang fully deformed from the loins of Seventh Day Adventism. Between them, the creationists and the militant secularists (who cannot believe their luck, or the dollar value of the publicity handed to them by creationism) have transmuted dangerously the relationship between Christianity and evolution. From the ghetto of creationism and 'intelligent design', a small, rich and politically influential constituency of Christians bellow at the evolutionists in the language of the King James Version. The evolutionists dismiss the creationists as benighted and medieval, and have tarred the rest of Christendom with the same brush. 'Why', they say, 'should we begin to take Christianity seriously? Its proponents are wholly incapable of handling evidence.' Creationism has inoculated a whole generation against Christianity.

The overwhelming consensus of modern biology is that some form of evolution by natural selection is the main agent of change in the biological world. Not a single paper espousing creationism or intelligent design has ever been published in a peer-reviewed scientific journal. The creationists say that this is because of scientific Stalinism, and indeed biologists whisper things in private that they would not dream of uttering in public. Careers are quickly destroyed by apparent infidelity to the Darwinian orthodoxy. But this is not the reason for the absence of proper creationist publications. There are no proper creationist publications because there is no proper evidence for any of the creationist assertions.

The currently fashionable fig-leaf to cover the scientific naked-ness of creationism is 'intelligent design' (ID). It is an idea that paints a strange picture of God – a God who delegates most of the biological craftsmanship to natural selection, but then wanders around the world looking for things that natural selection could have missed or might have done better. He has been strangely selective in what he chooses to put right. Why choose the bacterial flagellum, but not the recurrent laryngeal nerve or the plaice's head?

Quite apart from the sheer oddness of the idea, ID invites some impossible inferences. Although there is a continuing and exciting debate about the mechanisms used by Darwinism, there is no doubt that Darwinism *does* operate. And it can potentially explain much of the biological world. It does not follow from this that there is a demonstrable absence of 'design'. But it does follow from this that the contentions of the 'intelligent design' theorists are wrong: it cannot be demonstrated that a designer is necessary.

Despite all this, belief in creationism and intelligent design is growing massively. The ideas have about 50 million adherents in the USA, and they have metastasised across the Atlantic. Churches that ten years ago would have laughed at the mention of creationism now have bookshelves groaning with glossy, expensively produced and unrefereed denunciations of all the achievements of modern biology. An August 2006 survey of British university students found that more than a third believed in either creationism or intelligent design.[1] And once you're in the creationist fold, it is hard to get out again. Not only are the creationist/intelligent design movements energetically evangelistic, they also protect jealously the orthodoxy of their members. The members are never exposed to the scientific consensus; it is regarded as demonic nonsense. It is a worrying sign that many hundreds of thousands are apparently convinced by the arguments in Lee Strobel's book *The Case for a Creator*, a series of interviews with creationists. One might have thought – no, one might have hoped – that the book would have the confidence to deal squarely with the objection to its basic premises. But no. And the lack of confidence is well justified.

This steadfast refusal to engage with Darwinism is not restricted to dyed-in-the-wool Texan creationists: it permeates academic theology too. 'To a great extent,' writes the theologian John Haught, 'theologians still think and write as though Darwin had never lived. Their attention remains fixed on the human world and its unique concerns. The nuances of biology or, for that matter, of cosmology have not yet deeply affected current thinking about God and God's relation to the world.'[2]

There is a growing intellectual apartheid – an impermeable wall between Christianity and science. That is a shame for science, and disastrous for Christianity. The wall is the work of those (the creationists and the Darwinian ultras) who parody both Darwinism and Christianity. It is built from hardened, sclerosed ideas. There is a deadly failure in both of the radically polarised camps to engage with the thrilling complexity of the real world. It is a sort of autism. Creationism and Dawkinsism are both so dreadfully *dull*. Dull solutions cannot possibly be correct: the problems posed by the world are so immensely colourful.

Things are not as neat or as quantifiable as the Darwinian ultras represent them as being. It is simply not possible to demonstrate either that natural selection has in fact produced everything that we see in the natural world, or that it could have done. There is plenty of room for other complexity-generators. The other candidates need not elbow natural selection out. Indeed, they plainly have not done so. They may process arm in synergistic arm with natural selection through geological time. One of those candidates has a reassuring character.

Whether or not natural selection is *the* force driving biological change, the problems raised by suffering, waste and predation remain acute. In some ways they are more acute if the creationists are right. If God willed the nervous system of the zebra to react in the way it does when a lion's teeth closes on it, and designed the lion to kill, the charge against him is more grave than if natural selection is responsible for the form of the biological world.

There are, however, some tentative answers to the charge.

I am surprised and alarmed by what I have found in the book

of Genesis. It is stranger and more radical by far than I have
ever imagined it could be. I never dreamt that it could suggest
the reconciliation between the Bible and the archaeological record
that is sketched out in chapter 9. For years I have looked, baffled,
at the astonishing fact that for tens of thousands of years a
type of man, as anatomically modern as I am, lived in Africa
and the Levant, yet lived entirely intuitively, without any of the
trappings of symbolic thought. And then, suddenly, behaviourally
modern man exploded into the world, and it was immediately
a very, very different place. It is all very odd.

I do not deal in any detail with the contentions of Old Earth
creationists. There are several reasons for that. First, Young
Earth creationists are louder and more media savvy, and more
people will have heard of them. Second, while Old Earth creationists will typically believe that the 'days' of creation represent
much longer periods, and that there were special acts of creation
peppered throughout geological time, there are many nuances
separating the various Old Earth creationist factions. Discussion
of those nuances would have cluttered further an already packed
book. None of those nuances shields Old Earth creationism
from the withering fire of modern biology. And third, very
broadly, with the exception of the evidence about the age of
the earth, Old Earth creationism faces the same problems as
Young Earth creationism, and is therefore discussed by implication anyway.

This book will have something in it to frustrate and annoy
everyone. The biologists will think that I have oversimplified
the biology. They are right. The non-biologists will think that
the scientific chapters are terribly heavy going: I expect they are
right too. Theologians will justifiably moan that I have
summarised too brutally some very big and complex ideas.
Non-theologians will cross their eyes in bewilderment at some

of those ideas, and wonder if they could not have been put more simply.

So, sorry to everyone.

Writing this book has not made me less angry. But I can now go for a walk without feeling dirty.

Charles Foster,
Oxford, September 2008

CHAPTER I

The Tangled Bank

It is interesting to contemplate an entangled bank, clothed with many plants of many kinds, with birds singing on the bushes, with various insects flitting about, and with worms crawling through the damp earth, and to reflect that these elaborately constructed forms, so different from each other, and dependent on each other in so complex a manner, have all been produced by laws acting around us. These laws, taken in the largest sense, being Growth with Reproduction; Inheritance which is almost implied by reproduction; Variability from the indirect and direct action of the external conditions of life, and from use and disuse; a Ratio of Increase so high as to lead to a Struggle for Life, and as a consequence to Natural Selection, entailing Divergence of Character and the Extinction of less-improved forms. Thus, from the war of nature, from famine and death, the most exalted object which we are capable of conceiving, namely, the production of the higher animals, directly follows. There is grandeur in this view of life, with its several powers, having been originally breathed into a few forms or into one; and that, whilst this planet has gone cycling on according to the fixed law of gravity, from so simple a beginning endless forms most beautiful and most wonderful have been, and are being, evolved.

(Charles Darwin, *The Origin of Species*, chapter 14)

Imagine, as Darwin did, a tangled bank. To magnify its beauty, brutality and complexity, imagine that it is in the tropics.

It is covered in writhing plants. They wrestle and barge each other. Their roots probe the earth, seeking to take water and nutrients from their neighbours. They do not steal, because nothing holds any title that can be violated. Each organism has what it possesses for the moment. Generally things are taken, not given. There are no rights.

The plants trap sunlight in sugar, and that makes them prey. They are crushed and ground between the teeth of herbivores, and their cells are smashed up by enzymes and bacteria in big fermenting tanks. The sunlight therefore flows for a while into the bodies of the herbivores. How long it stays there depends on many things. It depends on the acuity of the herbivore's eyes; on the efficiency with which sodium and potassium gates open and shut in the membranes of its nose nerves; on the integrity of the wiring linking its ears to its legs; on the strength of the tendons; on how fearful it is; on how fearful its parents were; on whether or not the night wind has caused a branch to fall in the path along which it bolts.

If it is caught, it may die quickly, or it may die very slowly. If it is a mammal, its nervous system will go on screaming in (so far as we know) very much the way that ours does until the thing (whatever it is) that made it a live rather than a dead mammal has fled or been extinguished. Probably, if it is a mammal being eaten by another mammal, the death will be relatively quick, because the continued life of a victim is an inconvenience for a predator. It makes the victim flounder around, which gets in the way of the feed. But on the way to the death there are dislocations, breaks and rips. The eyes roll. Death does not seem to be welcomed.

Sometimes the death is prolonged. In the stream running by the side of the tangled bank, a fish has been caught by a lamprey. Two weeks ago the lamprey attached itself to the side of the fish, like a large leech. Its grinding jaws eroded the fish's body wall, and the head of the lamprey, and most of its body, is now inside the body cavity, still grinding away, but destroying nothing vital. To kill would be to change desirably fresh fish to carrion. Only the lamprey's tail now waves in the water. The waving tail attracts a larger predatory fish. Both the lamprey and its victim are swallowed whole. They will be marinated in digestive enzymes and dissolved into the body of the larger fish.

Back on the bank, a vole is eating seeds made partly from the body of a weasel which had thrived five years ago on the vole's great-great-great-great-great-grandparents. The bank is a graveyard, seething with life. Everything is a cannibal. The whole place is profoundly and vitally septic. Take away the bacteria that coat everything, and the bank would weigh a lot less and would soon be a desert.

The bank is a culture of intimate interdependence. The vole needs the owl that kills it no less than the owl needs the vole. One of the hawk moth species on the bank has acquired transparent wings to pretend to be a bumblebee and, unlike most moths, has changed its schedule to fly alongside the bees during the day.[1] Some of the orchids have fashioned cups which fill with nectar to entice insects. When an insect lands, it depresses the landing stage. As the insect crawls towards the cup, the stage springs back up, trapping the insect. The only way out is past hanging baskets of pollen. The insect flies away full of sugar and dusty with sperm.[2]

There is someone watching all this, and describing it. He is a man. What he makes of it all will depend on what he believes about himself. But whatever he makes of it, he thinks that it is interesting and terrible. And something in him dislikes the idea of being eaten by worms.

If he is a typical creationist, he believes that the species on the tangled bank are broadly as they were when they were created by God six to ten thousand years ago (depending on how he reads the biblical chronologies).[3] There has been some speciation since, but only in the direction of degeneration – as the genome sheds information like confetti. Man himself has no familial relationship with any of the creatures of the bank, and the different species on the bank are themselves related only by the fact that they spill, rather than share, one another's blood. The horrors of the bank are the fault of primordial man, whose arrogant usurping of the divine prerogative corrupted, by an obscure spiritual mechanism, the whole of creation. All species were originally vegetarian,[4] and lived in happy co-existence – a proposition that of course assumes that plants are happy being eaten. Before Eve plucked the forbidden fruit there was no death, no pain and no predation. The water creatures, the birds and humans (but not, apparently, the plants or the land animals) were commanded to multiply.[5] The strategy for ensuring that there was not catastrophic overpopulation is not clear.

Depending on whether the creationist believes Genesis 1 or Genesis 2, he should believe either that man was spoken into existence after the animals,[6] and set over them as ruler; or that man was formed from the dust of the earth, before the creation of the animals, the plants, or even the first rainfall,[7] and that the animals were thought of originally as company for him.[8] Probably, though, in a way mysterious to most of us, he will believe both.

If the observer is a mainstream evolutionist, he is in many ways more mystical than the creationist. He believes, like Genesis 2, that he was fashioned from dust, but believes that it was stardust. He describes, and, if he is that way inclined, senses an intimate familial communion with all the animals and plants on the bank. His wondering fascination with the biochemistry of the bacteria means that he sees no slight in being called their cousin. His sense of the immense age of the world gives him an exhilarating chronological vertigo when he looks at the bank. He thinks that the universe was formed about 15 billion years ago, and the earth about 4.5 billion years ago. If he thinks that there is a God, his God must be very big and very old.

He thinks that conditions on the earth were for a long time incompatible with life, but probably thinks that life sprang into existence about as soon as it could – about 3.8 billion years ago. Life is not only tenacious and fecund once it exists,[9] but also seems to loathe non-existence.

If the evolutionist is honest, he has no idea how life began, and points out that evolution itself does not pretend to have anything to say on the subject.[10] He acknowledges that the promise shown by the 1953 Miller-Urey experiment that we all learned about at school (in which amino acids were formed by discharging lightning-simulating voltages through an atmosphere of water, methane, ammonia and hydrogen) has evaporated: most think that the experiment made unsustainable assumptions about the chemistry of the early earth. He thinks that early forms of life were unicellular. The genesis of the cell is again, if he is candid, a complete mystery, although there are some elegant hypotheses. He notes that the general direction of evolution has been towards increased size and increased complexity. Cells initially got together in loose conglomerations. The conglomerations then became organised, centrally directed, and so transmuted into multicellular organisms.

Several forces drove this magnificent white-knuckle ride towards complexity. The evolutionist will not agree with all his fellows about the relative contribution of the various forces, but there will be a fair degree of agreement. He will subscribe, along with almost all of the scientific world, to the neo-Darwinian synthesis.

Charles Darwin in 1869. Photo by J. Cameron.

In *The Origin of Species*, published in 1859, Darwin set out the idea of evolution (which everyone acknowledged had happened) by natural selection (which was the real novelty). The idea was outrageously simple. Thomas Huxley,[11] when he heard of it, is said to have slapped his forehead and said, 'How stupid of me not to have thought of that.' Darwin, through his round-the-world trip on the *Beagle*, his readings of Malthus,[12] his afternoon perambulations around the Sandwalk at Downe House, and his obsessive observations of worms, finches, rocks, beetles, men and everything else, had been compelled to the conclusion that since

many more individuals of each species are born than can possibly survive, and as consequently there is a frequently recurring struggle for existence, it follows that any being, if it vary however slightly in any manner profitable to itself, under the complex and sometimes varying conditions of life, will have a better chance of survival and thus be *naturally selected*. From the strong principle of inheritance, any selected variety will tend to propagate its new and modified form.[13]

HMS Beagle *at Tierra Del Fuego, painted by the onboard artist, Conrad Martens, during the* Beagle's *voyage, 1831–36.*

Darwin had no idea about the mechanism of 'the strong principle of inheritance'. It was supplied just seven years after the publication of *The Origin of Species* by the Austrian Augustinian monk Gregor Mendel and his pea plants. The peas indicated that the units of inheritance were physically discrete. They would later be called 'genes', and identified as the sequences of nucleotides on the DNA molecule that determine the amino acid sequences of, and therefore the characteristics of, proteins.

Biology starts from the presumption that I am the sum of my proteins, and then gets interesting.

Mendel's 1866 paper was forgotten during his own lifetime, but was rediscovered and dusted down at the start of the twentieth century. Darwinism, languishing for want of an explanation of heredity, acquired new energy and confidence. The fusion of Darwin's original thesis with the new science of genetics is what is described as the 'neo-Darwinian synthesis'.[14] The synthesis reformulated Darwin's thesis by defining selective advantage. A characteristic coded for by gene X was advantageous in evolutionary terms if it increased the incidence of gene X in subsequent generations.

Gregor Mendel, the father of genetics.

The ratios in Mendel's pea paper allowed some exciting and intimidating mathematics to perfuse evolutionary biology. If you knew the mechanism of inheritance, you could determine the expected incidence of inherited traits. If you then compared this expected incidence with the observed incidence in populations, you were looking at more or less dim reflections of the forces of change themselves. You could begin to make mathematically informed guesses about the power, and possibly the nature, of the forces.

All evolutionists agree that classic natural selection is one of the forces. Genetic change occurs in various ways: mutations (most of which are harmful, but some of which will be beneficial); genetic recombination through the normal process of sexual reproduction; gene duplication (particularly in plants and bacteria); regulator genes, which switch on and off and otherwise determine the function of other genes; the introduction of new genes from other populations, and so on. There is bitter and highly technical disagreement about which of these mechanisms of change is predominant. The disagreements are irrelevant for the purposes of our look at the bank. Everyone agrees that genetic change occurs, and that at least some changes are detected by natural selection, which then gets to work, altering the gene frequency in subsequent generations. The really interesting disputes relate to the sensitivity of natural selection in picking up the change, and its efficacy in turning its detection into a final verdict on the relevant gene. We have noted that Darwin wrote, 'any being, if it vary *however slightly* in any manner profitable to itself ... will have a better chance of survival and thus be naturally selected'. Much of modern evolutionary biology is concerned with how slight a variation can be before it attracts the approving or disapproving attention of natural selection, with the role of contingency, and with the ability of natural selection to fashion new species rather than merely altering existing ones.

It has to be said that natural selection, whether or not it is the sole or principal engine of evolutionary change, is surprisingly sensitive and powerful. A tiny change (for instance in the number of stripes on a snail shell) can result in a dramatic change in the chance of the snail being smashed and eaten by a thrush.

If natural selection is not the only thing producing change, what else might be? Various candidates have been put forward by orthodox science, but when their credentials are examined carefully, they all turn out to be chance, dressed up in various more or less exotic ways. This book will suggest another possibility. But there is nothing necessarily disreputable about chance. Our own anecdotal experience might lead us to prefer its candidacy. Genuine accidents, unavoidable by the most refined nervous system or most beautifully toned muscle, do happen. If you are at the pinnacle of the natural selective tree, your rigorously selected genes will not help you much if you are also at the pinnacle of an erupting volcano which smothers you in boiling lava. If the volcano has not erupted for a few million years, it can hardly be said that you were stupid to live there, and that the lava has sought out and dealt sternly with the genes making you stupid. Natural selection is very good at picking up the pieces; it is often pretty dismal at stopping the destruction in the first place.

The mammals were tiny, unimpressive creatures in the age of the dinosaurs. The extinction of the dinosaurs gave mammals their chance, and natural selection vigorously promoted the mammals. But natural selection did not direct the asteroid that may well have ushered the dinosaurs into the museums.[15] If the asteroid had not landed, would mammals ever have had the chance to rule the earth?[16, 17]

If our bank-gazing evolutionist has been brought up conventionally in biology (and particularly if he has been brought up in the UK), he will tend to look at all the attributes of the bank-dwellers through an adaptationist lens. He will assume that everything about the hawk moth is precisely the way it is because natural selection has decreed it that way. He will credit natural selection with a superb eye for detail and the sculpting hand of a Michelangelo. He will credit little to chance, and nothing to God. God is a hypothesis of which he has no need, and indeed he will happily quote Laplace's dictum when given any opportunity.[18] Chance produces the entirely random mutations which give natural selection something to get to work on, but natural selection is so assiduous at sifting the phenotypic nuances thrown up by mutation that it refuses to delegate to chance any of the sifting.

But if he has read a bit (and particularly if he has studied in the US), he might have embarrassing doubts about this monolithic adaptationism. Perhaps his capacity to harbour such heresies is a function as much of his psychology as his academic upbringing. He might think that nothing in the world, let alone in biology, is likely to be quite so straightforward. He might be prepared to rejoice in the tangles of the bank, and to think that they might not be comfortably accommodated within the straitjacket of a single thought. He might be excited rather than outraged to hear Stephen Jay Gould asking, 'What is wrong with messy richness, so long as we can construct an equally rich texture of satisfying explanation?'[19]

The 'satisfying explanation', though, remains an essentially Darwinian one. Natural selection might not hone as finely as Darwin and Dawkins like to think; instead of a stately, gradual march towards complexity there may be genuine stasis in the fossil record, followed by massive, innovative jumps; there may be plenty of characteristics that confer neither significant advantage nor disadvantage, and therefore flap happily and neutrally through evolutionary history, unrecognised by the supposedly infallible eye of Darwin; if we were to re-run the tape of biological history again, the outcome might look very different; we might sometimes be tennis balls of the stars rather than of our genes. But let's not try to pretend (as some creationists outrageously do) that

Gould was not a thoroughgoing Darwinist. And at first blush it looks as if God might be too. Allowing room for contingency on the bank does not edge natural selection from its central place. And even if contingency were enthroned there, contingency is not, or at least not obviously, another word for God. It is not even clear that a bank ruled by contingency allows more space for God than does straightforward natural selection. Natural selection is powered by selfishness, appetite, waste, pain and death. Chance just could not care less about anything using any of these fuels to power anything. Neither looks much like the kind of God the Christians talk about.

Darwin concluded:

> There is a grandeur in this view of life having been originally breathed into a few forms, or into one; and that, whilst this planet has gone cycling on according to the fixed law of gravity, from so simple a beginning endless forms, most beautiful and most wonderful have been, and are being, evolved.[20]

No doubt – but it is an icy grandeur, a grandeur that can be appreciated only if you are deaf to screams and inured to gore. It is not the sort of thing you want your children to appreciate. Dusk has fallen on the bank. Bats begin to flicker around the trees, hunting by sonar the moths that hatched that day in the undergrowth. They kill particularly the very young – those on their first wing-stretch. The evolutionist stares into the fire he has made, and starts to get introspective. He sees pictures in the flames. They suggest stories that he has never heard. He conjures ghosts from the shadows, and sees teeth that are not there. His guide has a headache: he gives the guide some paracetamol from the medical kit, and then wonders why. He looks up at the sky, and feels smaller. This is absurd, because he has a PhD from Harvard and knows very well that he is the same size as ever. He has had a good day, and feels thankful. But he does not know whom to thank, or why gratitude is appropriate. He is used to dealing with death – his PhD involved thousands of post-mortems on field mice – but in the dark he begins to think of his mother, who died ten years ago, and he starts to cry. He is embarrassed and turns his face away so that the tears cannot be seen. It does not seem right that she died, although, having had six children, her function as a gene replicator had been amply fulfilled. He remembers her kindness to him long after he had had his own vasectomy and ceased to be a reproductively relevant animal. He remembers too her love of water-colours, of Etruscan frescoes, of the poetry of Gerard Manley Hopkins and, worst of all, the novels of Nabokov, which he hated. These were all useless things.

He remembers how his mother had tenderly taunted his reductionism in a letter, quoting Nabokov the fanatical lepidopterist. Nabokov had said that moth mimicry was 'carried to a point of mimetic subtlety, exuberance and luxury far in excess of the predator's power of appreciation'.[21] He remembers how he had felt forced to disagree loudly with this quote for the sake of his creed, although he had secretly wondered the same thing himself. And he remembers how he had first become a biologist: how, before he had ever heard of genes, DNA or bell curves, he had collected beetles, writing their names in childish handwriting on labels stolen from school. He had given them individual baby names, too, and had stayed up at night seeing how the reading lamp made their iridescent backs shimmer. It was not the biggest or most impressive that he had liked best. He liked the smallest ones, and the ones with the best names, but most of all he had liked the collection as a whole, as a community, because in that community the individuality of each was seen best. He remembers how they had buried his mother; how the brothers had thrown flowers into the grave, and how, although the sun was bright, the world was black.

Early next morning the evolutionist looks out of his tent onto the bank, sees a snake snatch a fledgling, and knows that whatever nonsense had come into his head in the night, the presumptions in his PhD were right all along.

CHAPTER 2

A Tale of Two Cities and Two Bigotries

Town twinning represents a unique and dense network . . .
(European Commission, *Town Twinning*)

North Oxford is a rich and genteel place, a land of opulent Edwardian villas with well-manicured trees and book-lined studies. Improbably beautiful girls with huge brains and huge bags of books cycle down the Woodstock and Banbury roads to the Bodleian Library. Its children, endowed heavily by their genes and their environment, tend to proceed effortlessly to one or other of the ancient universities.

It is the home of Tolkien, punts, intimidating bridge parties, cellars of ancient Burgundy, endless Nobel Prize winners and captains of industry, and Richard Dawkins.

North Kentucky is neither rich nor genteel. The best way to get there is by flying to Cincinnati/North Kentucky International Airport. If you drive seven miles along the I-275 freeway you get to the Creation Museum, the flagship of the Young Earth creation movement 'Answers in Genesis', whose stated aim is to 'exalt Jesus Christ as Creator, Redeemer and Sustainer', to 'equip Christians to better evangelise the lost' and to 'challenge visitors to receive Jesus Christ as Saviour and Lord'. Every employee has to sign a statement of faith that reads, 'Scripture teaches a recent origin for man and the whole Creation . . . the great flood of Genesis was an actual historic event . . . [and] no apparent, perceived or claimed evidence in any field, including history and chronology, can be valid if it contradicts the Scriptural record.'

The Creation Museum, North Kentucky.
A human and a dinosaur living happily together.

Inside the museum, built at a (presumably pre-Copernican) astronomical cost of $27 million, eighty animatronic dinosaurs, many of them side by side with well-groomed primordial humans, roar at the alarmingly numerous visitors who pour through. One triceratops wears a saddle; another, along with a stegosaurus, peers sullenly out of a scale model of Noah's ark. DVD presentations spell out the surprisingly far-reaching consequences of rejecting the creationist view of Scripture. A miserable girl, whom we assume took modern geology seriously, talks about her abortion. An unhappy teenage boy, who presumably doubted the museum commercial's suggestion that Eve rode on the tail of a brontosaurus, sits slumped in front of his computer, corrupted by internet pornography.

North Oxford and North Kentucky are vastly different, yet

there is a curious measure of agreement between them, and a strange synergy.

Dawkins and the Young Earth creationists both think that one simple idea explains everything in the world. For Dawkins, it is evolution by natural selection. No corner of the universe is unilluminated by Darwinism. It determines not only how spiders weave their webs, but how bards weave their myths, the physical universe its fabric, and ministers their sermons. If we are kind, it is actually because we are selfish, and kindness increases our chances of reproduction.

For the creationists, the grand and simple idea is that the universe was created, exactly as it says in one or other or both of the Genesis stories, six to ten thousand years ago, in a literal week. Failure to understand this metastasises dangerously into all areas of life. If one can treat the first two chapters of the Bible with the contempt inherent in saying (for instance) that the days of creation were not normal twenty-four-hour days, the authority of the rest of the Bible is catastrophically diluted by human reason and imagination. Allow metaphor a foot in the door, and it will take over the whole house, and then where will we be? But exclude from Genesis the possibility of poetry, symbolism, myth (how they hate that word!) and metaphor, and the Bible becomes as straightforward a manual for human living as the instructions for erecting a picnic table. There is no need to consider (and indeed one must not consider) cultural or historical context, literary form or apparent scientific contradiction. If the Bible says that 2 + 2 is 5, then 5 it is, regardless.

Dawkins and the creationists agree, importantly, about something else. They both agree that the theory of evolution by natural selection excludes the existence of God. They are natural allies. The creationists are Dawkins's best friend – and not just because he is able to make fun of their scientific naiveties. Where would Dawkins be without them? He would be a tenured professor at Oxford, known by middle-class intellectuals for his clever, beautifully written and waspish books, appreciated on mid-morning highbrow radio, and frustrated by his lack of real celebrity. There have always been a few people who think, like he does, that natural selection elbows God out of the universe. Until the birth of the creationist movement they were regarded as interesting, slightly off-the-wall fanatics whose wild theological extrapolations indicated a disreputable departure from their real area of expertise. But because a loud, well-financed and energetic movement agrees with Dawkins's basic premise, they have given him undreamt-of prestige, coverage, book sales and theological authority. For millions of his gullible, scientifically uneducated disciples, the premise now appears to be scientific orthodoxy. Creationism has done untold harm to Christianity, and untold good to Richard Dawkins's bank balance.

Richard Dawkins lecturing on his book The God Delusion.
Photo: Matthias Asgeirsson.

If it were not so sad and so damaging, the battle between North Oxford and North Kentucky would be fun to watch. The creationists denounce Dawkins as the handmaiden of Satan; he dismisses their propaganda as 'the drivelling ephemera of juvenile pamphleteers and the cold preaching of spiteful old hardliners'.[1] Once he has started, of course, he is difficult to stop. It is not just the Young Earthers who get the rough end of his very lucrative tongue – it is everyone who does not think that the religion of science says everything that is true about the world. He gets carried away with himself, and he gets away with it because he is very smart and very entertaining. From the fairly self-evident truth that creationism should not be taught in high school science classes, he gallops wildly on to insist that theology has no place in a modern university and that the chaplain should be banished from the Oxford high table. And his camp followers go baa-ing behind him in uncritical agreement.

As a phenomenon, then, Dawkins is a creature of the creationists. His essential creed – scientism – has a quaintly dated feel about it. Since H.G. Wells, few outside Communist Russia really articulated it until Dawkins did. For most intellectuals in the last two thirds of the twentieth century, reductionism was a tendency against which to warn overzealous science students, not a creed to embrace.

Creationism itself is a very recent movement. Until it reared its head, evolution and Christianity cohabited perfectly happily. The Church has taken in its stride (with a few unfortunate stumbles) everything that science has come up with. One would hope that this is no surprise: both science and the Church are, after all, supposed to be in the same business of uncovering and expounding the truth.[2]

Christianity has generally been a beneficiary, not a victim, of scientific discovery. For more than a thousand years the governing cosmology was Ptolemy's: the earth was at the centre of the universe, and all the heavenly bodies rotated around it in circular orbits. But by the sixteenth century this model was insupportable. Mars was in the wrong place. So Copernicus and Galileo remodelled the universe: the earth and the other planets rotated around the sun. The shift took some getting used to. Some insecure conservatives in the Church behaved badly for a while, but soon came to terms with it. It was quickly noted that the new Copernican universe was vastly bigger than Ptolemy had thought. God was correspondingly bigger too. The only casualties of the Copernican revolution were some inaccurate Ptolemaic equations and some overparochial notions about God. Both were far better dead. And yet Galileo would find it hard to get reasonably priced life insurance in modern Kentucky.

It is perfectly true that there was a crisis of faith in Victorian England. But it is historical gibberish to attribute it to Darwinism. It started long before the publication of *The Origin of Species* in 1859. The geological research of Charles Lyell and others had shown that the earth was immensely old, and that man was a recent arrival. The Industrial Revolution had scooped great chunks out of England, ramming geological antiquity down the pious throats of the Victorians. Railway cuttings, canals and quarries forced them to acknowledge that they were living on top of an ancient mortuary. It was the fact of animal death on a previously unimagined scale and over a previously unimagined timescale that reduced the zeal with which some educated Victorians sang their evangelical hymns. Tennyson expressed their doubts:

> So careful of the type? But no,
> From scooped cliff and quarried stone
> She cries 'A thousand types are gone:
> I care for nothing, all shall go.[3]

The worry was that the God who was supposed to have made all the 'types' seemed to be so indifferent to their extinction. It was the problem of animal pain, waste and death that unsettled the Victorians, not the problem of natural selection itself. And Tennyson was writing in 1850.

It is popularly thought that the publication of *The Origin of Species* precipitated a wide and persistent rift between biological and Christian orthodoxy. It was not so. The roots of the misperception probably lie in the only tale of *The Origin*'s initial reception that is commonly cited – the famous and acrimonious clash in Oxford between the sanctimonious Bishop 'Soapy Sam' Wilberforce, self-appointed Defender of the Faith, and 'Darwin's Bulldog', Thomas Huxley. The bishop sarcastically asked Huxley whether it was 'through his grandfather or his grandmother that he claimed descent from a monkey'.[4] Huxley is supposed to have turned to Sir Benjamin Brodie, whispering, 'The Lord hath delivered him into my hand,' before rising to his feet and delivering the devastating retort, 'If then the question is put to me whether I would rather have a miserable ape for a grandfather or a man highly endowed by nature and possessed of great means of influence and yet employs these faculties and that influence for the mere purpose of introducing ridicule into a grave scientific discussion, I unhesitatingly affirm my preference for the ape.' The myth says that the Church, routed in the Oxford debate, ran cravenly off into ever-deepening creationist conservatism and irrelevance, sniping vainly from the margins into the main intellectual camp, ever thereafter held stoutly by the Darwinist forces of enlightenment.

'*Darwin's Bulldog*', *the biologist Thomas Henry Huxley. Artist Carlo Pellegrini.*

But it was not like that. It is surprisingly difficult to work out just what happened in Oxford, but the perception of most contemporary observers was apparently that the evening was inconclusive and amicable. The rival factions may even have gone off arm in arm to dinner afterwards. Certainly mainstream Victorian Christianity appears to have accommodated Darwin's insights fairly comfortably. Darwin sent a complimentary copy of *The Origin of Species* to the Rev. Charles Kingsley. Kingsley replied, thanking Darwin, and noting that although he had not yet read the book, he had already 'gradually learnt to see that it is just as noble a conception of Deity, to believe that He created primal forms capable of self-development' as it was 'to believe that He required a fresh act of intervention to supply the lacunas which He Himself had made'.[5] This was a typical Christian response.

This accommodation persisted, more or less, until the last few decades of the twentieth century. Of course there were always people who insisted on a literal seven-day creation,[6] but in Europe, by and large, they did not bother the evolutionists, and the evolutionists did not bother them. In the US there were occasional clashes, the most notable and shameful being the 1925 Scopes 'Monkey' Trial, a judicial lynching in which a high-school teacher was convicted by a Tennessee jury of teaching the godless theory of evolution. But even in the US the perceived centrality of creationism to Christian teaching is a recent mutation.

The roots of modern creationism go rather further back. Its pedigree is soundly Seventh Day Adventist. The founder of Seventh Day Adventism, Ellen G. White, claimed to have been shown by God in a vision in 1864 that he had created the world in six twenty-four-hour days, and that the fossils were all artefacts of the Noahic flood. These ideas were promulgated by George McCready Price in his *New Geology* (1923), and taken up, popularised and transmuted into the Young Earthers' canon by Henry Morris. 'Is it possible to be a Christian evolutionist?' Morris notoriously asked. 'Yes,' he concluded: 'Just as one can be a Christian thief, or a Christian adulterer, or a Christian liar. It is absolutely impossible for those who profess to believe the Bible and to follow Christ to embrace evolutionism.'[7] There was nothing new about the thought. What was new was the epigrammatic way in which it was expressed, and the energy and money put behind its publication. It is interesting to note that Richard Dawkins would agree wholeheartedly and without caveat with Morris's comment.

Morris's remark was designed to offend and provoke, and it did. It was a comment of such stultifying stupidity that it raised emotional temperatures all round. It was not the sort of comment about which one could remain genially neutral. It polarised and divided.

Many Christians, particularly but not exclusively in the US, agree with the remark. It has become a defining article of Christian belief. To them, the issues are tremendously simple. There is no need to spend a long time agonising over the evidence accumulated and accepted by science. For $9.97 I became the proud owner of *Disprove Darwin in 5 Minutes or Less*, beamed electronically to me from Delray Beach, Florida. It seemed like a remarkable bargain. It promised that it would enable me to 'tear apart the "theory" of evolution, and win every debate, every time'. It would give me 'everything you need to take on the skeptics and win. You'll never be at a loss for words. The whole evolution debate will be right in your pocket. Use it anytime, anywhere . . . it's *much* easier than you think. Once you get the real story, it takes less than 5 minutes!' (original emphasis) And what, exactly, would I be able to do? I would be able to: 'quickly take down self-righteous atheists'; 'easily and accurately defend God's role as our Creator'; 'send hardened skeptics into a state of confusion'; and 'expose the "theory" of evolution and leave scientists with their mouths hanging open'.

It is perfectly true that efforts like this have left scientists 'with their mouths hanging open'. But not with horror that their carefully constructed biological edifices have come tumbling down, or in worship of the awesome God they suddenly see. Their horror and surprise has been at the apparent inability of creationism to see or evaluate the evidence, and at what they see as the consistent misrepresentation of the various schools of thought.

Stephen Jay Gould was particularly (and eloquently) irritated by this. He was always an unrepentant Darwinist, but had developed the theory of 'punctuated equilibrium' (the notion that there is often real stasis in the fossil record, interspersed with times of rapid change). Creationists had often tried to recruit him onto their side. This was very wrong, and Gould hated it:

> Since we proposed punctuated equilibrium to explain trends, it is infuriating to be quoted again and again by creationists – whether by design or stupidity I do not know – as admitting that the fossil record includes no transitional forms. Transitional forms are generally lacking at the species level but they are abundant between larger groups.[8]

Others are even more forthright: 'In all of these efforts [to promote creationism in schools] the creationists make abundant use of a simple tactic: they lie. They lie continually, they lie prodigiously, and they lie because they must.'[9]

These unedifying comments are quoted simply to demonstrate that there is a war on. The history shows that it is a war almost entirely of the creationists' making, and it is a war in which the principal casualty is the intellectual credibility of Christianity. Although most European Christians and vast numbers of US Christians repudiate violently the crass pastiche of Christianity painted by creationism, it is not surprising that they get tarred with the same brush. Creationism misrepresents Christianity.

The new Darwino-atheists, captained by Richard Dawkins and Daniel Dennett, are delighted at the misrepresentation. They have mainstream Christianity in their sights, not just that wing of it which sounds off in demonstrably erroneous ways about matters within the true province of evolutionary biology. One can understand anyone wanting to protest at the assertions of North Kentucky, but why spend a career denouncing regular, moderate, Darwin-believing Christians of the sort who read

The Voyage of the Beagle with admiration and simply have the effrontery to think that there are more things in heaven and earth than were dreamt of in *The Selfish Gene*?

There has been a good deal of not particularly interesting speculation about the origins of this zeal. Some like to see Dawkins as a puppet of hell; others, burrowing deep into his childhood, have erected elaborate Freudian theories. Some suggest cynically that an attack on all the Christians in the world sells more books than an attack only on those who believe that all the animals did indeed troop into the ark. But whatever is going on in his psyche, there seems absolutely no reason to doubt, and every reason to believe, that Richard Dawkins is utterly sincere. He is a true believer.

It is tempting to say that he is a Darwinian fundamentalist. Many have given in to the temptation. But it is not quite true. He is a fundamentalist all right, but not a Darwinian one.

Like many fundamentalists, Dawkins believes that his creed is the original one, the pure one; that he drinks from the source, whereas others drink from the contaminated water further downstream. As we have already noted, he believes, too, that the single pure idea of which he is a consecrated custodian has a unique, messianic, explanatory and saving power. It explains all, and it saves from all error.

A single explanatory principle would be very nice. It is the Holy Grail of biological science. Richard Dawkins thinks that Darwin found the Grail somewhere between the Galapagos and Kent. But the reason why Dawkins is not a Darwinian fundamentalist is that Darwin himself did not claim anything like as much for his own work as Dawkins does. Indeed, he expressly disavowed what his earnest disciple is now claiming in his name. In the last edition of *The Origin of Species* (1872) Darwin wrote:

As my conclusions have lately been misrepresented, and it has been stated that I attribute the modification of species exclusively to natural selection, I may be permitted to remark that in the first edition of this work, and subsequently, I placed in a most conspicuous position – namely at the close of the Introduction – the following words: 'I am convinced that natural selection has been the main but not the exclusive means of modification.' This has been of no avail. Great is the power of steady misrepresentation.[10]

Great indeed. So great that an entire school of predominantly Oxford-based biologists – the ultra-adaptationists – spent their lives, framed their equations and preached their sermons on the basis of a view of the Master's teaching which he had specifically repudiated.[11] For them, natural selection explained everything about the biological world. The spots on the tail of a bird of paradise were in the orientation that they were because that arrangement increased the chance of copulation with a fertile mate. The apparently gratuitous flamboyance or whimsy of nature had, if you looked hard enough through your Darwinian lens, a stern utilitarian explanation.

This was the school where Richard Dawkins learned his evolutionary grammar. It was a very English school. The English tended, at least until quite recently, to overvalue order, even at the expense of the right answer. An English schoolboy in the 1950s would be better off writing neatly the wrong answer to his sums than writing the correct answer in a spidery hand on a page covered with blots. And even if he could write neatly, he would be well advised to avoid eccentric creativity. It was the philosophy of the parade ground and the barrack room. Straight lines and straight trouser creases were what life was all about. A wrinkle met with the wrath of the drill sergeant. Ultra-adaptationism is the biological equivalent of the trouser crease.

Of course one could forgive the adaptationists for giving natural selection a status denied to it by Darwin if the subsequent evidence showed that to be justified. But precisely the opposite has occurred and continues to occur. Almost nobody in biology doubts that the Darwinian paradigm is *broadly* correct, but the whole history of biology since Darwin has been a history of wrinkle-generation. The basic paradigm is in no danger at all of toppling – it acquires strength with every new bit of information that comes in – but it is becoming more complex. It is an impressive testament to the robustness of Darwin's original thesis that it has the elasticity to accommodate all the new data.

This makes it all the more sad and strange that, precisely at the time when the evidence is compelling evolutionary biology to act creatively and imaginatively to accommodate the nuances thrown up by the real world, the adaptationists are becoming more and more sclerotic. Stephen Jay Gould, as ever, put it well:

What an odd time to be a fundamentalist about adaptation and natural selection – when each major subdiscipline of evolutionary biology has been discovering other mechanisms as adjuncts to selection's centrality. Population genetics has worked out in theory, and validated in practice, an elegant, mathematical account of the large role that neutral, and therefore nonadaptive, changes play in the evolution of nucleotides, or individual units of DNA programs. Eyes may be adaptations, but most substitutions of one nucleotide for another within populations may not be adaptive.

Why then should Darwinian fundamentalism be expressing itself so stridently when most evolutionary biologists have become more pluralistic in the light of these new discoveries and theories? I am no psychologist, but I suppose that the devotees of any superficially attractive cult must dig in when a general threat arises. 'That old time religion; it's good enough for me.' There is something immensely beguiling about strict adaptationism – the dream of an underpinning simplicity for an enormously complex and various world. If evolution were powered by a single force producing one kind of result, and if life's long and messy history could therefore be explained by extending small and orderly increments of adaptation through the immensity of geological time, then an explanatory simplicity might descend upon evolution's overt richness. Evolution then might become 'algorithmic', a surefire logical procedure, as in Daniel Dennett's reverie. But what is wrong with messy richness, so long as we can construct an equally rich texture of satisfying explanation?[12]

What does all this mean for our debate? Certainly not that natural selection is not a major sculptor of organisms: it is. But it does diminish the credibility of the most vocal high priests of natural selection (notably Dawkins and Dennett) when they seek to extrapolate from their own discipline into other arenas. It indicates that they are religious men. They should be treated with the suspicion appropriate to all religious men, and their pronouncements viewed as religious assertions rather than scientific theorems. North Oxford turns out to be just as religious a place as North Kentucky. When North Oxford and North Kentucky talk about God, they each have it disastrously wrong, and for the same reason.

The error is that neither treats the account in Genesis with anything like the respect it deserves. That account needs a serious look. But so, first and briefly, does the science.

CHAPTER 3

Who's Right? Evidence and the Lack of It

When on board HMS *Beagle*, as naturalist, I was much struck with certain facts in the distribution of the inhabitants of South America, and in the geological relations of the present to the past inhabitants of that continent. These facts seemed to me to throw some light on the origin of species – that mystery of mysteries, as it has been called by one of our greatest philosophers. On my return home, it occurred to me, in 1837, that something might perhaps be made out on this question by patiently accumulating and reflecting on all sorts of facts which could possibly have any bearing on it. After five years' work I allowed myself to speculate on the subject, and drew up some short notes . . .

(Charles Darwin, Introduction to *The Origin of Species*)

'True' and 'false' seem often to be offensive categories – and certainly, if the only virtue is tolerance, they are. If Young Earth creationism is true, neo-Darwinism is false, and vice versa. There is no room for both of them. And we should not decide who has it right by measuring the volume of their sermons, the intensity of their zeal, the sales of their books, the number of their biblical references or their ability to sway US presidential elections.

This is an unambitious chapter. It claims to be neither authoritative nor comprehensive, but only to sketch the outlines of the evidence for and against two positions: evolution by natural selection and Young Earth creationism. The basic claims of those schools have been summarised in the previous chapters. This chapter touches too on the idea of intelligent design.

It has two objects: to see, when we look at Genesis, (a) whether Genesis purports to cover the same ground as that roamed over by evolutionary biologists, and (b) if and to the extent that it does, whether there are contradictions between the scientific account and the biblical version. Young Earth creationists pour millions of dollars into research, and often say that science vindicates them. Are they right?

You will not find much argument in this chapter; it is mainly a display of exhibits.

First, though, some preliminary points.

Metaphors, and how to kill and skin them

We have already noted that there is an understandable but dangerous desire for a single, simple solution to all biological problems. The creationists call that solution God; Richard Dawkins calls it natural selection. Humans, wired though they are to manipulate complex ideas, seem to be uncomfortable with complexity. The tendency needs to be watched. If the desire for simplicity seems to be a *driver*, be suspicious. By all means use Ockham's razor in its proper place, to distinguish between competing ideas.[1] Be very wary of using it as a presumption about the number of or nature of the ideas likely to explain an entirely mysterious phenomenon. Wielded there it is likely to cut throats, not cut crap.

Many of the gladiators in the evolutionary arena are far more splendid writers than they are scientists. Many of them have a wonderful way with metaphor. Metaphors can illuminate; they can also intoxicate and fog. Lay people, presented by a scientist with a dazzling metaphor, are unlikely to know the limits of its usefulness.

Three examples. The first, beloved of the creationists, was coined by the astrophysicist Fred Hoyle, who likened the probability of (for instance) a mouse being assembled by natural selection to the probability of a fully functioning Boeing 747 being assembled by a gale blowing through a junkyard.

It is a glorious picture, but it wholly misrepresents the contentions of the evolutionists. They all agree that the chance of a mouse being assembled overnight from its raw materials is so vanishingly small that the idea can be confidently and contemptuously dismissed. What is wrong with Fred Hoyle's metaphor is that it is not about natural selection at all. Chance, as already explained, is very, very far from being the whole naturally selective story. Chance (through random mutation, genetic recombination, etc.) provides the substrate upon which natural selection gets to work. The possibilities thrown up by chance are then pushed through a fine sieve. What gets through is by no means random: it is that which confers an advantage – defined as something which increases the incidence in the population of something like itself.

The elementary fallacy in Hoyle's metaphor was thoroughly and brutally exposed by Richard Dawkins's 'Weasel Program'.[2] It was directed specifically against the 'infinite monkey theorem' – the idea that there is nowhere near enough time for a randomly typing monkey to bash out all the works of Shakespeare. Creationists use the picture as a basis for asserting that there is nowhere near enough time for mere chance to produce the natural world. Fair enough, said Dawkins, let's not be so ambitious. Let's take, not the whole Shakespearean corpus, but just one short sentence from *Hamlet*: 'Methinks it is like a weasel.' The number of possible combinations of the component letters is 27^{28} – about 10^{40}. If a computer does the 'typing' instead of the monkey, even if the computer generates millions of combinations per second, it is unlikely that, even if it ran for the entire lifetime of the universe, the desired phrase would ever be produced. If, however, you tweak the program so that the computer begins by choosing a random sequence of 28 letters, then randomly 'mutates' the sequence and selects, each time, the version which, however slightly, most resembles 'Methinks it is like a weasel', the computer reaches the target phrase very quickly – over lunchtime, when the program was written in BASIC; in 11 seconds when it was written in Pascal. What it illustrates is the crucial difference between single-step selection and cumulative selection. Darwin's whole point was that natural selection is cumulative.

Of course the Weasel Program has its limitations – the most obvious being that a human mind (a 'designer's mind') chose the end phrase, and accordingly this is really a model of how evolution can realise a template that already exists. But these quibbles misunderstand: the program was never intended to be a comprehensive model of evolution. Better models have been developed for that.

The second metaphor comes in the title of Richard Dawkins's book *Climbing Mount Improbable*.[3]

Dawkins's Mount Improbable is a forbidding mountain, rearing out of a plain. It has a clearly unscaleable face, and many similarly impossible peaks. On the top of each peak is a biological marvel. On one is the mammalian camera eye; on another the echo-location equipment of dolphins; on another the ability of swifts to navigate from the Congo to the English home counties. And so on.

The observer stands on the plain, looking up at the mountain in awe. How on earth did each of the marvels get there? They plainly could not have climbed up the face, or jumped up in a single great bound, and apparently there is no other way up. He concludes that they must have been placed on the pinnacles by a great Force in the Sky.

And then (I am adapting Dawkins's metaphor slightly, but only in a way that he would like) the now-religious observer is tapped on the shoul[der]... beckons him to follow. ... of the mountain. From th[e] back of the awesome face, ... sloping foothills climbs all th[e]... There is another way up, if you ... ually there. No great gravity-defyin[g]... mountaineering skill; and no sky-hook[s]... The back route is the path of natural... man, of course, is Darwin.

This is all good stuff, but all that the We[...] the brilliant, powerful, useful metaphor of Mo[...] really say is that Fred Hoyle was badly wrong, an[d]... to show anyway. They do not say (as lay evolutionists – not Dawkins himself – often try to make them say) that natural selection *can* get you to the top of each of the pinnacles, or that nothing else could get you there. Both of those (very distinct) propositions can only be asserted (if they can be asserted at all) after an exhaustive and exhausting audit of the evidence relating to the explanatory power of natural selection and its competitors. We embark on a highly abbreviated version of that audit shortly. But finally, the third metaphor – or, better, pejo-rative epigram.

This is Richard Dawkins's phrase 'selfish gene'. It is an arresting phrase. We relate to it, and give it a respect out of all proportion to its reflection of biological realities, simply because of the anthropomorphic adjective. We understand the word 'selfish' better than we understand most of the other things in the biology books. We feel intellectually more comfortable with it than with the esoteric machinations of the Krebs cycle. And we readily adopt things that we think we understand. But although millions have been seduced into accepting the image because of its apparent accessibility, how many, if pushed, have

THE SELFLES[S]

any real idea what th[...] (comprehensible[...] makes th[...] It m[...]

phrase asserts? The fact that 'selfish' is linked to 'gene' (barely comprehensible) whole package even more seductive. It is flattering. akes us think that by using it we are initiated into some esoteric mystery. And so it is used widely and uncritically. It has become a sort of biological tic. Indeed, if there are 'memes', the expression 'selfish gene' is my first candidate for meme-dom. This is superb scientific salesmanship,[4] not least because the apparently easy comprehensibility implies that if you do not grasp the idea fully, you are dumb. It is a way of seeing off hard questions.

One of the hard, yet blindingly obvious questions that it tends to stifle is about how sharp a sculpting tool natural selection really is: how acute is its view of the genome. Sometimes you feel really stupid asserting that natural selection works at the level of the whole organism – not least because Dawkins of course agrees, loudly and contemptuously, as if only a really retarded student who somehow slipped through the Oxford admissions net would bother to make such a basic observation. But it is worth remembering, nonetheless, as we move towards our look at the evidence. Natural selection, Ian Tattersall reminds us, is a 'one shot deal':

What determines the reproductive fate of [your] offspring could be anything, but it will most likely be their overall viability. You can be as smart as you want, but it won't do you much good if you are too slow at escaping from predators … In the end, natural selection has to vote up or down on the success – in living or in reproducing – or actually both – of the entire individual, not of its separate features. It cannot tease out subcomponents to favour or eliminate. There is no proportional representation here; the election is strictly first past the post. Inevitably, then, we have to get away from the popular notion that evolutionary change consists essentially of a process of fine-tuning of individual characteristics. It simply cannot be. Individuals must succeed or fail – or reproduce successfully, or don't, warts and all . . .[5]

'Yes, yes,' drawls the bored Dawkins. 'Let's get on, shall we?' So let's get on.

Common ground?

Is there any common ground between the evolutionists and the creationists?

They both look out on the same biological world (although it often does not seem like that), and both seek to explain its history and its present constitution.

Note, importantly, that both of them believe in evolution. What they disagree about is the *extent* of evolution. The creationists accept that there has been change over time in living organisms. It can hardly be denied. The beef served in the diner on the way to the Kentucky Creation Museum has been hacked out of the buttocks of a cow demonstrably different from its less efficient predecessors. It is the result of clever selective breeding. A chihuahua has little in common with a bull mastiff apart from the fact that they are members of the same species – they are both domestic dogs. Similar things happen in nature. But creationists say:

1) that the direction of evolution since the animals spilled out of Noah's ark has been downward – in the direction of degeneration. This downward trajectory is a consequence of the fall. No *new* information has been added to organisms – information has instead been lost.

2) that while evolution may have produced (possibly, even, by natural selection) organisms that look different from anything

else that has existed before, these are related to the ones produced by God in his one-off design process (and preserved on the ark) in the same way as the chihuahua is related to the mastiff. Micro-evolution (change *within* species) occurs and can readily be demonstrated. Macro-evolution (the production of radical new types, more complex than the ones from which they sprung) does not occur and has never been demonstrated. We have to be careful about saying (as is often said) that creationists claim that there has been no *speciation*. We return to that issue shortly.

The evolutionists, of course, believe that evolution has generated massive complexity. While macro-evolution has never been seen in living organisms, that is not surprising. Human life spans are too short. But, they say, it is a reasonable, indeed compelling, inference that micro-evolution, if it goes on for long enough, will produce new species.

Some of the evidence relating to speciation is examined below. There is really very little common ground.

Falsifiability: Darwinism and creationism

This is no place to discuss the various theories about what constitutes science. They matter very much to some people, but not to us. We do not care much whether or not Darwinism or creationism deserves the fairly arbitrary label of 'science'. We are only interested in which of the two, if either, is true. The only reason to mention the issue is because, sensibly deployed, the theories can sometimes uncover humbug. Sometimes they generate it, but sometimes they expose and prick inflated claims about what a particular hypothesis can do. It is enough for now to say that a commonly deployed and useful criterion is falsifiability.[6] If they are practising proper science, scientists exist in a state of perpetual nail-biting uncertainty, since it is by definition possible for their cherished theories to be definitively, fatally contradicted by new evidence. Proper science is vulnerable.

Do the theories of evolution by natural selection (Darwinism) and creationism pass this test of definitive vulnerability?

Certainly some central tenets of Darwinism do. Haldane,[7] asked what would disprove Darwinism, replied, 'A rabbit in the Ordovician.' He was right. If tomorrow's newspapers reveal that a fossil rabbit has been discovered from the Ordovician era, before the first land plants, insects, amphibians or reptiles, Darwinism will be dead, biology will have no ruling paradigm, and everyone will go baffled back to the drawing board. If dinosaur footprints are found superimposed on human ones, North Kentucky will be entitled to cheer, although it would not prove their case: chronology alone can devastate their case; it cannot make it.

There are other areas of potentially fatal vulnerability which make Darwinism falsifiable. Darwinist gradualism needs a very great deal of time. If the earth were shown to be only ten thousand years old, Darwinism would simply be wrong.

Darwinism predicts things. If those things can be shown to be absent or impossible (always difficult to do, for anything), then the part of the paradigm that predicted them will be redundant. It is now that we run up against the difficulty of trying to describe as a single monolithic concept something as complex as Darwinism. Darwinism is not like a three-legged stool – so unstable that the loss of any one of its legs will cause it to fall.

Darwin predicted, for instance, that transitional forms (species representing intermediate stages en route to a known later organism) would be found in the fossil record. Creationists say that no such forms have been found *or are there to be found*. Darwinists disagree. We will look at the evidence later. But suppose the creationists are right: does that mean that the whole of Darwinism should be ripped up? It does not. It could mean several things. It could mean that the intermediates were so unstable that they were simply not around for long enough to be represented at all in the fossil record. It could mean that they were not around in circumstances kind to fossilisation. It could mean that Darwin was wrong about gradualism, and that evolution occurs by massive, sudden changes (by colossal mutations or wholesale disorder in the gene switch-box) rather than by slow, incremental change. Would this latter suggestion invalidate the theory of evolution by natural selection? Of course not: it would merely put some spikes in the otherwise smooth curve representing the progress of evolutionary change against time. The new organism would still be a significant milestone in the evolutionary journey for the same reason that less dramatically modified organisms are: because it had been tested by natural selection and allowed to contribute some part of itself to a subsequent dynasty.

The question of the falsifiability of other elements of Darwinism is more contentious, more technical, less interesting and less relevant. We return to some of those elements later, in a less aridly philosophical context. All that need be said here is that at present the tools available for measuring the *force* and therefore the explanatory power of natural selection are crude. If that force cannot be accurately measured, it cannot be accurately correlated with the amount of change seen in the environment. If it cannot be accurately correlated, it cannot be said that natural selection is so suspiciously good a fit that one can imply causation rather than mere correlation. Still less can it be said that it is so obviously the sole candidate for 'cause' that all other candidates can be confidently dismissed. But in principle, if not yet in practice, it *may* be possible to establish confidently that natural selection does not have a hand in shaping the biological world at the moment, so satisfying the criterion of falsifiability. With the caveats above (re the time necessary for natural selection to work), it is unlikely to be possible to falsify the *past* claims of natural selection.

What, then, of Young Earth creationism?

In many ways, creationism is similar to Darwinism in terms of falsifiability. If the earth is older than ten thousand years, the Young Earth element of creationism is a fairy story. If it could be shown conclusively that dinosaurs and men did not inhabit the earth at the same time, the thesis would explode. If it could be shown that animals suffered and died before there were any men to fall, that again would be the end of creationism. But God himself is notoriously invulnerable to disproof. And if he cannot be disproved, neither can the hypothesis that he operated in any particular way. If, indeed, he is omnipotent, omniscient and transcends time, he *may* have warped time or otherwise changed the rules, somehow telescoping 3.8 billion years of evolutionary time into ten thousand years of earth time. He *may* have planted the fossils in their strata as a massive joke with which to amuse himself and the faithful, and to confound ungodly scientists. It does not seem like him, somehow, but omnipotence is certainly a handy get-out-of-jail card for a creationist in a tight argumentative spot. All of which goes to show only that the philosophy of science does not help much, and we should rush on to the evidence itself.

Falsifiability: intelligent design

Before leaving falsifiability altogether, it is nonetheless worth seeing what it can do with intelligent design (ID). This is particularly so since ID insists loudly that it is a kosher science (and therefore ought to be taught in school science classes).

Most ID adherents accept that Darwinian natural selection

is an adequate (or at least not a demonstrably inadequate) explanation for most of the biological world. But they draw the line at some structures and processes. These, they say, are so complex that natural selection could not possibly have designed them. They necessarily require the hand of an 'intelligent designer'. Almost all of them identify the designer with God – although they often do not say so expressly.

It takes only the slightest acquaintance with the notion of falsifiability to realise that ID does not even begin to satisfy it. All that ID says is:

a) In the present state of knowledge we cannot understand how structure X evolved.
b) We cannot think that anyone in the future will be able to understand it either. It is *in principle* (but what principle?) incomprehensible.
c) Therefore something other than the presently described mechanisms must be involved.
d) What is involved can be nothing less than a *deus ex machina*.

Step (a) is appropriately humble: hopefully all scientists are capable of it. Step (c) is plain and trite. But (b) and (d) are not only absurd, but patently unfalsifiable. As to (b), the whole history of science is the history of previously unthinkable discoveries. As to (d), why identify the mechanism with God? How can it possibly be shown that the mechanism will not be something that turns up next week in a laboratory in Japan? Indeed, as we will see, the whole unhappy history of ID is the history of allegedly incomprehensible structures being explained perfectly satisfactorily in PhD theses. When this happens the high priests of ID, apparently undaunted, go off in search of more as-yet-unfathomable mysteries on which to hang their cult, and the faith of the congregations seems untouched.

What is the significance of the theoretical discovery in Japan?

If a naturalistic mechanism is demonstrated, this rarely shows that the structure *had* to be constructed by that mechanism, but simply that it *could* have been – that the previously incomprehensible is now in theory comprehensible. A designer is not necessarily excluded by such discoveries. And a designer is certainly not necessarily included by the absence of such discoveries.

ID should certainly be taught in schools. It should be taught in the marketing classes. It is a superb example of how, if you package an idea (like a shampoo, a skin cream or toothpaste) in pseudo-science, people will buy it.

The age of the earth

We live in a universe of unimaginable, terrifying antiquity. The available evidence suggests that the universe itself is about 14 billion years old. How do we know this? Because on a clear night, with a decent telescope, we can peer back in time at something fairly close, in relative terms, to the time when the universe exploded into being. We are constantly bombarded by breathtakingly ancient photons. We know that most of the distant galaxies are more than 10 billion light years away, and yet we can see them. We know how fast light travels. We therefore know that the light hitting our retinas left those galaxies at least 10 billion years ago, and accordingly the universe must be at least that old.

Is that an end of Young Earth creationism? Well, it should be, since on most Young Earth constructions of Genesis God created the universe *ex nihilo*, and the earth either at the same time or within a couple of days of it. But there is a lot at stake here, and a good deal of ingenuity and money has been lavished on trying to stop the creationist horse falling at the first fence.

One of the creationists' primary and more comprehensible

contentions is that the speed of light has not been constant: they claim that it is now a lot slower than it was.[8] This would mean that light from the furthest corners of the universe reached us more quickly than it would at today's speeds – taking years off the age of the universe. Thus Barry Setterfield has asserted that six thousand years ago the speed of light was millions of times greater than it is today. This would mean that the universe was a mere fifteen thousand years young.[9]

The contention has never been published in any peer-reviewed journal, and has never received any support from mainstream science. Any change in the speed of light of anything approaching the required magnitude would massively destabilise matter. As has been pointed out in some genuinely impressive creationist contentions, if the physical constants of the universe were even slightly different from what they in fact are, the observed universe would be wholly impossible. We are on a mathematical knife edge, from which some (with force) infer a designing intelligence.[10] Setterfield would tip the universe over the edge into non-existence.

The earth itself is a relative newcomer to the universe. Most believe it to be about 4.5 billion years old. Creationists, to survive, have to reduce it to about ten thousand years. They do this by asserting that the methods conventionally used for measuring the earth's age are simply and dramatically wrong. To get an idea of just how wrong they must show conventional science to be, consider an analogy. I generally consider myself to be 6 feet 3 inches tall (1.905 m). To come to that conclusion, ordinary rulers have been used. But suppose those rulers were in fact wrongly graduated at the factory, and wrongly graduated by the same degree as the conventional dating methods must be wrong in order for the creationists to be right. If the rulers were wrong in one direction, I would be 2,812,466 feet (857,250 m high).[11] That is almost 100 times the height of Mount Everest.

Well, perhaps I am, but it seems unlikely. Take another analogy: if I am slow, and all the traffic lights are against me, it takes me five minutes to cycle from home to the library. Or at least I think it does. If my watch is wrong to the same degree as the creationists say the evolutionists' clock is wrong, it actually takes me 4.28 years of non-stop cycling.

One of the major tools used for dating rocks (and therefore the organisms found in them) is radiometric dating. The basic idea is simple. Different isotopes of the same element have different properties. Some isotopes are stable: they do not decay by emitting radioactivity. Unstable, decaying isotopes are useful: they are the ticking hands of the most commonly used geological clocks. Uranium-235 is a good example. It decays to lead-207, with a half life of 713 million years. There would be no uranium-235 on an infinitely old earth: it would all have changed to lead-207[12]. Since there is an alarming amount of uranium-235, we can be confident that we live on a planet that had a start.

Now, lead-207 is not the only form of lead. There is another lead isotope, lead-204. It has nothing to do with uranium-235. Imagine, then, that an igneous rock is being formed. Uranium-235 is assimilated into it, and the uranium decays at a known rate to form lead-207. The proportion of lead-204 to lead-207 allows us to calculate the time when the rock was formed.

There are other isotopic clocks working on similar principles. About forty independent systems are used. The commonest are potassium-40, which decays into argon-40, and rubidium-87, which decays into strontium-87.[13]

Now here is the important thing: they all agree broadly with each other. Yes, there are minor discrepancies, but the discrepancies are nothing approaching the magnitude that they would have to be to squeeze the age of the earth and the geological layers on it to the tiny size necessary to leave the Young Age creationists still in the game. Remember the supra-Himalayan Charles Foster. Creationists often snipe at anomalous individual results. One tale that gives incomprehensible comfort to creationists is the result of dating from the eruptions at Mount St Helen's. Ten-year-old lava was apparently isotope-dated at between 0.35 and 2.8 million years old.[14] But it hardly helps. Can *all* the techniques be *always* wrong, by so many orders of magnitude?

Creationists have begun to face the problem squarely and bravely, in the only way possible – by suggesting that the rates of isotope decay have changed over geological time. It is precisely the same strategy we saw when examining the issue of the age of the universe and the speed of light: if the constants embarrass you, make them inconstant. But there is a problem with simply saying that the rate of decay was hugely faster in times past and has gradually slowed down to the rates we see now. This is that the new postulated decay rate throughout most of the six to ten thousand years of Young Earth time would have released levels of radioactivity wholly incompatible with life. It would mean that the earth, for most of the last (and demonstrably fecund) ten thousand years, was a 1945 Hiroshima, not a garden.

Ever ingenious, the creationists have risen to the challenge by suggesting that the isotopes disgorged most of their radioactivity in two huge pulses – one at the time of creation (after which the rate fell to zero), and one at the time of the flood (after which the rate fell rapidly to the low level we now see). The evidence has not risen similarly to the challenge. There is no evidence whatever to support the suggestion.[15]

Being as kind as possible, it is impossible not to note that the creationist ideas about the age of the earth are contradicted by every single piece of evidence available. Here are just two more.

The bristlecone pines on the eastern slopes of the Sierra

Nevada are the oldest known trees. Their annual rings tell us that the oldest is about 11,800 years old, and carbon-dating agrees. Were tree rings accumulated more rapidly in times past? Was the Sierra Nevada caught in an Einsteinian time warp?

Trees older than this were engulfed by the last ice age, but ice tells its own story. That too is a story of immense age. There are seasonal ice strata, rather like tree rings, laminating the depths of ice sheets. They go back (measurably) 180,000 years. Lake beds similarly stratify seasonally: the oldest reliably dated layers are 35,000 years old.[16]

And so on and so on. The evidence, coming from all directions and from many sources wholly independent of one another, indicates that there is far too much antiquity for Young Earth creationism, yet arguably enough for natural selection.

Trends in evolution

In the rest of this chapter we look at some representative samples of the evidence that confronts anyone, whether creationist or evolutionist, trying to understand why the world is the way it is. But before doing that, let's pull back a bit and look at three big themes, three apparent trends in evolution: increased size, increased complexity, and convergence.

It must be noted that the creationists will generally not acknowledge any of these as a trend. If you only have six to ten thousand years to play with, you do not have much time for patterns to emerge. If species are basically fixed, subject only to the disorganising corruption of the fall, the only likely trend is towards simplicity, dissolution and the reduction of the total amount of information in any given biological system. The occurrence of any contrary trend at all is accordingly evidence against creationism.

It will be objected (and the objection is fair) that this discussion assumes the truth of one of the basic pillars of the Darwinian paradigm – namely that there is a demonstrable family tree (or, more accurately, a shaggy, unkempt bush) in the fossil record; that C somehow emerged from B, which in turn sprang out of the antediluvian loins of A. I do indeed assume it for the moment, as does almost everyone in the field. We look later at some of the objections to the assumption.

If the conventional interpretation of the evidence is right, organisms have gradually got bigger and more complex. Size and complexity are often related, although not necessarily. An elephant is more complex than an amoeba, but a shrew is more complex than a bank of coral. If you have a bigger body, you generally need a more sophisticated control centre to make it do the things that natural selection smiles upon. The higher up the evolutionary bush the Tertiary mammals climbed, for instance, the heavier, on average, they tended to be – 9.1 per cent larger, in fact, than their congeneric ancestors.[17]

Although it is harder to measure, complexity also seems to blossom more abundantly the nearer the top of the bush you are. I am the descendant of a self-replicating molecule that somehow appeared more than 3.5 billion years ago, and even with all due modesty and even on a bad day, I am a great deal more complicated than it was. If one added up all the biological complexity on the earth and translated it into sound, the noise of the earth would be an exponential crescendo, starting from silence. It is almost silenced at the times of the great extinctions, but rapidly builds again.[18] It now deafens, although with man's avarice threatening to wipe out species at a rate that dwarfs the Permian extinction, it may soon fall back to a terrifying silence. Whether the noise is generally harmonious or discordant is the subject of another chapter.

If biological life is a symphony, the third theme, convergence, is the constant recapitulation of a cadence or an air, but with this crucial difference: the air appears to have been rewritten entirely from scratch each time. This is indicated by two basic facts. First, there are often slight but distinct differences between the snatches of tune which indicate independent authorship. And second, the tunes are found in places so far from each other that communication between the authors can confidently be discounted.

Imagine a dolphin and a shark. Their basic body designs are very similar indeed, and yet they are wholly different animals. Dolphins are mammals; sharks are ancient cartilaginous fish. Many of the Australasian marsupials look very similar to the corresponding placental mammals outside Australasia. One would be hard pressed to distinguish between the dentition of the extinct marsupial sabre-toothed cats of South America and the placental sabre-toothed cats of Asia and North America. Dogs and cockroaches walk – both mechanically and neurobiologically – in astonishingly similar ways. The North American star-nosed mole has a nose which is fantastically sensitive to touch. The neural wiring of its nose is very, very similar to the wiring of the human eye. This is a mole that uses its nose as an eye. Yet none of the animals in these paired examples has shared a common ancestor for many, many millions of years.

What is going on? The creationists would say that the answer, on the evidence so far presented, is straightforward. Rembrandt had certain ways of doing things – certain mannerisms with his brush – which to an expert make his paintings, even when they are of very different subjects, unmistakably *his*. The similarities between the shark and the dolphin are the distinctive brush strokes which tell of divine artistry. That is the way in which God chose to do things. And, because he is a consummate professional, the designs happen also to do beautifully the job for which they are designed.

But the more carefully we look, the more difficult it is to sustain this answer.

In many quite obvious and important ways, we are not at all like cephalopods (octopuses, squids and cuttlefish). But our eyes are *almost* identical. They are both camera eyes. They have a slit at the front to let light in, a lens to send the light in the right direction, and a layer of photoreceptive cells upon which the light falls and which convert the light to nervous impulses which pass to the brain.

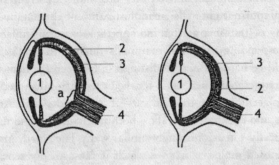

The mammalian (left) and the octopus (right) eye compared.
1: Lens. 2: Retina. 3: Nerve fibres. 4: Optic nerve. a: Blind spot.
Jerry Crimson Mann (modified Vaclav Horky: GNU Free
Documentation Licence).

Many disparate organisms, in fact, have very similar camera eyes. It seems clear that camera eyes have evolved entirely independently at least seven times, and very possibly many more than that. 'Rembrandt,' says the reassured creationist. But it is not that easy. The problem lies in the '*almost* identical'.

The light that shines round the edge of a lens is slightly more bent than the light passing through the middle.[19] In an efficient camera eye, such as that possessed by an octopus or a man, this is done by passing the light through some crystallin proteins, so adjusting the light's refractive index. The crystallins used by men and octopuses have an identical effect on the refractive index. Men and octopuses solve the problem in precisely the same way. But although the proteins are functionally identical, they are wholly different proteins.

If you are an evolutionist, this is exactly what you would expect. Evolution recruits what it needs from whatever is available. For the creationist, it is a problem. We have superficially similar pictures, but from different eras and with demonstrably different brush strokes. Can common authorship still be asserted?

'Of course it can,' the creationist rejoins. 'This simply shows that God has a big palette and impressively versatile technique. He can make use of all sorts of colours and methods. You shouldn't assume that he's as ploddingly predictable as human artists.'

Very well. But there is yet another problem. The vertebrate eye does not seem to be the work of a consummate artist. It is not optimally designed. The photoreceptors point it in what seems to be the wrong direction – away from the light, and towards the retina. This means that the neural cell layer, which sends the visual images from the retina to the brain, is between the light and the photoreceptors. This reduces the sensitivity of the photoreceptors, and creates a blind spot where the axons leave the neural cells on their journey to the brain. We know that there is a better solution, because that solution is seen in cephalopods.[20] There, the order of the layers is how you would expect it – how you would design it. In fact, as we will see, there are many examples of very obviously suboptimal design in the natural world.

Although it seems immensely unlikely, convergence occurs at the molecular level too.

If one has (as we have on this planet) a carbon-based biochemistry, it is vital to be able to split CO_2 apart. This is done using the enzyme carbonic anhydrase. It now seems as if carbonic anhydrase itself has evolved independently at least five times.

What are we to make of all this? On the face of it, truly

independent convergence, with slightly different designs and the odd bit of suboptimal design, tends to tip the balance away from a single Rembrandt-like author. It tells us something, too, about the power and downright vitality of natural selection. To design something complex once is impressive: to do it twenty times without any reference to the way it was done before is pretty awesome. But it may imply, too, that there is a limited number of possible solutions to the problems thrown up by the world. What we do with this observation is philosophically interesting. It makes some people rankly Platonic, talking about the world's gradual alignment with the unseen Forms. Such thoughts are easily translated into an (unsatisfactory) Christian mysticism. But at the very least it may imply that there is more directionality to evolution than we might initially have thought. Despite the apparently clear role of chance in the process of natural selection, we might be going somewhere after all.

What does the fossil record say?

The graveyard on which we live is a well-organised one. It is more like a multistorey car park for corpses. Each level represents a different age. Bore down through the crust, and every twist takes you deeper into time. The journey will be more or less the same whether you are drilling in Arizona or Zimbabwe. Of course there will be some variations – the history of Arizona and Zimbabwe are not quite the same – but the overall picture is well established and acknowledged even by most creationists. The successive strata are collectively known as the geologic column. Creationists, of course, dispute the dates given to the strata. Their contentions are worth a closer look.

Very broadly, there are four great geological divisions: going from the (classically) oldest to the youngest, these are the Pre-Cambrian, the Palaeozoic, the Mesozoic and the Cenozoic. In

EON	ERA	PERIOD		EPOCH	DATES*	AGE OF EVENTS	
Phanerozoic		Quaternary		Holocene	0–2		Humans
				Pleistocene			
	Cenozoic	Tertiary	Neogene	Pliocene	2–5	Mammals	
				Miocene	5–24		
			Paleogene	Oligocene	24–37		
				Eocene	37–58		
				Paleocene	58–66		
							Extinction of dinosaurs
		Cretaceous			66–144		Flowering plants
	Mezozoic	Jurassic			144–208	Reptiles	1st birds/mammals
		Triassic			208–245		First Dinosaurs
	Paleozoic	Permian			245–286		End of trilobites
		Carboniferous	Pennsylvanian		286–320	Amphibians	First reptiles
			Mississippian		320–360		Large primative trees
		Devonian			360–408	Fishes	First amphibians
		Silurian			408–438		First land plant fossils
		Ordovician			438–505	Invertebrates	First Fish
		Cambrian			505–570		1st shells, trilobites dominant
Proterozoic		Also known as Precambrian			570–2,500		1st Mulitcelled organisms
Archean					2,500–3,800		1st one-celled organisms
Hadean					3,800–4,600		Approx age of oldest rocks 3,800

* Note: Dates are in million years.   Taken from *Modern Physical Geology*, Graham R. Thompson Ph.D., Jonathan Turk Ph.D., Saunders College Publishing

The Geological Column.

the geological column these are almost always found sequentially arranged, with the 'oldest' at the bottom and the 'youngest' at the top.

Each of these great divisions (and the subdivisions within them) has a visibly distinct fossil fauna and flora. You get dinosaurs in the Mesozoic; you get none at all in the younger Cenozoic. For the evolutionist, of course, this is entirely what one would expect. Lots of Palaeozoic animals are not seen after the Palaeozoic. Evolution had moved on. Natural selection had handed the baton to others. The inference is that the older forms gave rise to the younger ones. But the creationist has a problem: he typically believes that all the animals and plants found in the Palaeozoic, the Mesozoic and the Cenozoic were on the earth at the same time.[21] They all arrived in 'Creation Week'. But why, then, is the fossil record not a well-mixed, exuberant cocktail of Palaeozoic, Mesozoic and Cenozoic life? Why do Mesozoic dinosaurs not share their final resting place with Palaeozoic trilobites?

The creationist response is to say that the Palaeozoic, Mesozoic and Cenozoic systems were different, geographically distinct, but contemporary ecosystems. If one looked at the fossils from a contemporary rainforest, a contemporary coral reef and a contemporary city, one would see very different things. Well, true, but if they were contemporary but geographically separated, they would not lie neatly on top of one another, always in the same order wherever one looked in the world. If the creationists were right, you would find a mass of Palaeozoic fossils in Europe, a mass of Mesozoic fossils in North America, and so on. But you do not. The problem is compounded for the creationist since the flood is supposed to have buried everything at the same time.

If we accept the conventional (and intuitively correct) approach that deeper is older, what does it tell us? It tells us that for much of the 4.5 billion-year history of the earth, it was lifeless. From 3.8 billion years ago we begin to see the first biochemical footprints of life. The first organisms we know about were bacteria. They thrived, they birthed everything that there is, and they still thrive. If we judged by influence, antiquity, weight, or most other criteria of significance, any proper history of the earth would be written from their perspective.

For a very long time, only single-celled organisms crawled across the planet, although they became increasingly complex single cells, packed with increasingly impressive biochemical assembly lines. And then, really quite recently (about 1000 million years ago[22]), we see community: cells conglomerate. At first these early communities were simple, naive communes. We do not know what was in it for the members, although there are plenty of speculations. Finally, about 580 million years ago, there is evidence, largely in the form of tracks, holes and burrows, for a much more sophisticated form of cellular community.[23] These were the first discrete multicellular organisms. They were soft, they fossilise well only under unusual conditions, but they were distinctly there, creeping through the Pre-Cambrian slime.

It is worth emphasising this, because many creationists deny that there is any evidence of Pre-Cambrian life. This is often because they want to make more of the so-called 'Cambrian explosion' than it really deserves. They want to see it as an explosive Genesis event, in which life suddenly burst out of a sterile darkness.

The so-called 'Cambrian explosion' is a perhaps misleadingly dramatic term to describe what is simply an unprecedented load of marine fossils – unprecedented in their numbers and their complexity. Although there is a real and vibrant debate about the nature and significance of the Cambrian explosion, it was not the start of life. There may conceivably have been no explosion of biomass or complexity at all: the period may simply have been one in which fossils were better formed than they had been earlier. But this would be an eccentric view. Most people agree that something significant happened then. It is often said that almost all the animal phyla we know are known from the Cambrian. But it is not quite true. There is a caveat that may or may not be significant: almost all the known animal phyla *with good fossil records* are known from then.

Why did it happen? Again, we do not know. Perhaps a key gene evolved. Perhaps the total amount of DNA somehow snowballed, multiplying possibilities which were later realised under the greater selective pressures applied by faster, nastier animals with the first hard parts. But however it happened, it was an exciting chapter.

Why did the excitement not continue at the same pace after the end of the Cambrian? There is no doubt that it did not. Indeed, it has been wisely suggested that what really needs to be explained is not the Cambrian explosion, but the post-Cambrian slowdown.[24] Perhaps the biological creativity of the

Cambrian had been so immense that all the workable basic design plans had already been tried out. Perhaps all the niches were already filled with organisms so splendidly tailored to their environments that they could laugh at any truly novel challengers.

All this happened in the sea. Thereafter, and fairly fast, we see evidence of freshwater life (about 440 million years ago) and spores which probably indicate that, for the first time, there were land plants. It is not until the Devonian period (400 to 360 million years ago) that the land became a really busy place, but no animals other than insects and other arthropods left the water totally behind until the reptiles emerged at the end of the Carboniferous (about 300 million years ago).

The air was colonised by flying reptiles in the Jurassic (200 to 140 million years ago): they joined the already ancient winged insects. True birds (really a form of modified dinosaur) and mammals got their big chance after the annihilation of the dinosaurs (and a lot else) by a large lump of rock landing on Mexico. They made the most of it.

Thus bacteria spawned shrews, and shrews were among the first of a mighty dynasty. This was a dynasty of hairy animals whose young fed by sucking on modified sweat glands. They tended to be most at home on land, although some of them went back to the water, remastering it. Very, very late in the day, somewhere in Africa, one member of the dynasty hoisted itself onto its hind legs. It had a peculiarly mobile thumb, a particularly big brain and some other even more curious characteristics. We return to it later.

We have said that X gave rise to Y, but what evidence is there for that? In many cases, of course, X is still around. There are still plenty of bacteria. This observation grounds the traditional creationist question, much lampooned by evolutionists: 'So, you think we came from monkeys, eh? So why are there still monkeys swinging through the trees?' Nobody who has read this far will need that question answered, but it remains the fact that mere succession in time does not imply familial relationship. I was born after Charles Darwin died: that does not in itself mean I can claim him as family. And if one is talking about the later being in some sense *better* than the earlier, the continued existence of the earlier might tend to militate against familial relationship.

But in fact there are several reasons to suppose that X gave rise to Y. Some of the most compelling lie, as we will see, in the genes. But two broad reasons nestle too in the fossil record.

The first is one of overwhelming impression. In early deposits you get very basic sharks. In later deposits you get much more refined sharks, and the basic sharks very often disappear. It never, ever, happens the other way round. If the creationists are right, and speciation is a degenerative process, it should always happen the other way round.

The second is that, just as Darwin predicted, and despite the creationists' howls of protest, you see transitional forms – forms bridging the gap between a more basic X and a more refined Y. It is correctly argued that when we look at the fossil record we *generally* – not exceptionally – see transitional forms: that all the species in a particular line of descent are examples of it. But there are more dramatic examples than this. Six instances among very many make the point.

1) In Western Australia in 2006, *Gogonasus* was discovered – a 380-million-year-old fish which may be the ancestor of all tetrapods. Its skull has large holes in the top, which may have allowed it to breathe through the top of its head, but most significantly it has muscular front fins with a well-formed humerus, ulna and radius.

2) The creationists have long contended that the curious skull

of the flatfish could not have evolved incrementally. In 2008 intermediate forms en route to the modern position were found: *Amphistium* and *Heteronectes*.

3) Evolutionists predicted that rudimentary feathers would be found on some dinosaurs en route to becoming birds: they duly were, in the Chinese *Dromaeosaur*.

4) Twenty-six species of primitive 'walking whales' – mammals in the process of returning to the water from terrestrial life – have now been described, many of them from Pakistan.

5) The tale of the evolution of the equine limb from the first, poodle-sized proto-horse, *Hyracotherium* (55 million years ago: four toes on the front limbs, three at the back), via *Mesohippus* (40 million years ago: three and three), *Pliohippus* (15 million years ago: one and one) and several other inter-mediaries to the earliest *Equus* (probably about 4 million years ago) is neatly filed in the record. Indeed, it is so neat that many creationists have given up on it, choosing to dismiss it as insignificant.[25] (Of course the story itself, as opposed to the record, is not at all neat. Few things in evolution are. It is a messy story of trial and error, with lots of dead ends.) If the intermediate stages were not known, however, creationist textbooks would be full of diagrams asserting derisively that toes cannot be transmuted magically into hoofs.

6) Mammals are generally thought to have emerged from a subgroup of the reptiles, the cynodonts. Throughout their history the cynodonts look increasingly like mammals, but they had one particularly interesting characteristic, buried deep inside their heads, and well fossilised. Mammals have three middle ear bones – popularly called the hammer, anvil and stirrup. Reptiles, including the cynodonts, have a much more basic hearing system, and have only one middle ear bone. But very close to it are two other bones, the quadrate and the squamosal, which act as a hinge between the upper

and lower jaw. In mammals the hinge is constructed from two entirely different bones, the dentary and the squamosal. Now here's the thing: immediately before the mammals emerged, there lived a subgroup of cynodonts with *two* jaw hinges. The first was a mammalian-type squamosal-dentary hinge; the second was the classical cynodont hinge. But this second hinge was squashed up very close to the eardrum: it seems that it was transmitting vibrations to it. We have here a transitional middle ear. The overwhelming consensus is that gradually this second hinge was allowed to work exclusively as a vibration-transmitter, leaving the other hinge to get on with opening the mouth.[26]

That said, there are periods in the fossil record that look pretty much like stagnancy, and they are often followed by the abrupt

A creationist car in Athens, Georgia, asserts that the fossils say 'no' to evolution. Copyright Amy Watts.

59

appearance of a palaeontological novelty. This might be a genuine novelty (we have discussed already the notion of punctuated equilibrium, a hypothesis which assumes that the apparent stasis and sudden pulse of morphological novelty are real), or it may be an artefact of a fossil record that we know to be incomplete. Most things did not fossilise, although if you were a marine animal with hard parts you had a much better chance than an earthworm. It is a wonder that we have as much as we do. Whether real or artefactual, the stasis is not anything to keep a properly informed Darwinist awake at night.

The strange case of the coelacanth is a cautionary tale to be noted well by anyone worried about the alleged dearth of transitional forms.

Coelacanths are bony fish, important because of their relationship to the first creatures to crawl onto land. They appear in the fossil record for nearly 350 million years, finally (and apparently definitively) bowing out about 65 million years ago. But on 23 December 1938 the trawler *Nerine* returned to port at East London, South Africa, after trawling around the mouth of the Chalumna River. As he often did, the skipper, Hendrik Goosen, telephoned Marjorie Courtenay-Latimer, the curator of East London's museum, to see if she wanted to look at his catch in case there was anything interesting. She came, and lying at the harbour she found a fish she later described as 'the most beautiful fish I had ever seen, five feet long and a pale mauve blue with iridescent silver markings'. Baffled and fascinated, she searched the books in vain for an identity, and then tried to contact the South African ichthyologist Professor James Brierley Smith. He was away, and so she wrote to him, including a crude sketch of the fish. The letter did not reach him until 3 January. When he saw the sketch, he later wrote, 'A bomb seemed to burst in my brain . . . I told myself steadily not to be a fool, but there was something about that sketch that seized on my imagination and told me that this was something very far beyond the usual run of fishes in our seas.' He could not get through to Courtenay-Latimer by telephone until the next day. He waited a nail-biting three hours for the call to go through, only to be told that the internal parts of the fish had been dumped out at sea, along with the rest of the town's festive rubbish. In the meantime the rest of the fish had been preserved by a local taxidermist. Brierley Smith finally got to East London on 16 February. He raced to the museum: 'Although I had come prepared, that first sight [of the fish] hit me like a white-hot blast and made me feel shaky and queer; my body tingled. I stood as if stricken to stone. Yes, there was not a shadow of doubt. Scale by scale, bone by bone, fin by fin, it was a true Coelacanth.'[27]

The coelacanth species found in South Africa (*Latimeria chalumnae*), while extremely rare and highly endangered, has since been found also in the Comoros, Kenya, Tanzania, Mozambique and Madagascar. A second species (*L. menadonesis*) was found in Sulawesi, Indonesia, in 1999.

Why the absence in the fossil record for 65 million years? It is thought that coelacanths, which are now found only in very deep water, became extinct in shallow water. Fossils from deep-sea waters are only rarely recovered.

It is hard to be a creationist palaeontologist. As well as fishing boats trawling up embarrassments, every spadeful of earth from a major excavation increases your load of explanation. So far, no boat and no spade has produced anything helpful.

What things look like

HOMOLOGY

Bat wings, killer whale fins, zebra limbs and human hands do very different things, and yet they all share the same basic structure.

This indicates a common ancestor, say the evolutionists. No, say the creationists, it is another example of a Rembrandt brush stroke.

VESTIGIAL ORGANS

I am sitting in a library, and I am sitting on my tail. This is rather strange, because the collection of coccygeal vertebrae does me no very obvious good at all.

Some snakes have pointless, functionless legs, visible on X-ray. Many cave-dwelling animals, blind for aeons, have non-functioning eyes.

Why? The pointless things are a quaint inheritance from our ancestors, who found them useful, say the evolutionists. No, say the creationists, they have a use, even if we cannot understand it now. They may be right about some of the organs often

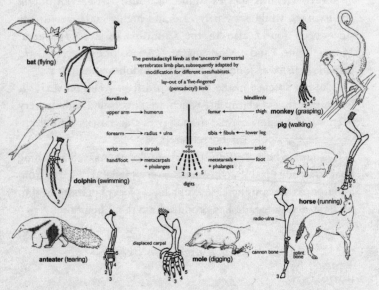

Homology in the pentadactyl limb: Jerry Crimson Mann (GMU Free documentation licence).

dubbed 'vestigial'. The human coccyx seems to act as an anchor for some muscles important in defecation.

It is harder not to credit the ancestors for many of the other alleged bequests, though. And hard indeed to say that many apparently vestigial structures are the sort of thing that God might have put there out of sheer artistic exuberance. The iridescent wings of a hummingbird are one thing; a mammalian appendix, lying apparently inert and occasionally deadly at the junction of the colon and the caecum, is quite another.

EMBRYOLOGY

Many biology textbooks still assert that we have all been fish, and much more recently than the Palaeozoic. Indeed, they say

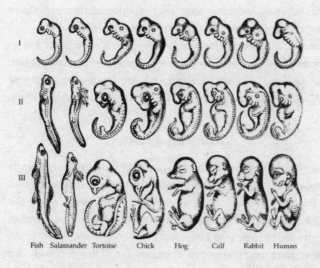

I

II

III

Fish Salamander Tortoise Chick Hog Calf Rabbit Human

Romane's 1892 depictions of Ernst Haeckel's now discredited embryo drawings, used to support Haeckel's 'recapitulation' thesis, and unwisely deployed by Darwinists to support the idea of descent from a common ancestor.

that when we were gestating we had gill slits, and lived out in utero a fair amount of our alleged evolutionary history. This is the notion of 'recapitulation', championed by the result-faking German biologist Ernst Haeckel,[28] and should form no part of modern debate about the truth or falsehood of evolution.

It is certainly true that an early human embryo is notoriously difficult to distinguish from that of any other vertebrate. The gill ridges were actually called visceral clefts. Had I been a fish, they would have turned into gills. In fact they turned into part of my auditory canal. This confirms nothing.

What was embryological sauce for the Darwinian goose was also sauce for the creationist gander. The creationists legitimately observe that even closely related species (for instance of sea urchins) follow dramatically different developmental paths. That, they say, indicates that they do not share a common ancestor. Their inference is just as wrong as Haeckel's.

The sauce of recapitulation is simply not very good sauce. Far better evidence of the relationship between organisms lies, as we shall see, in the alarming and comforting similarity of my DNA with that of all other living organisms on the planet.

Where things are

In his wanderings with the *Beagle*, Darwin was particularly impressed by where organisms were and where they were not. The most dramatic examples that he gave were from the Galapagos Islands. They have perhaps been drained of some of their drama by repeated citation.[29]

Other than being dropped there by God, the only way for terrestrial animals to get to really remote oceanic islands is to fly there. Before humans arrived in New Zealand, the only animals there had wings (although some of their wings had not been used for flying for millions of years). If God were involved *directly* in the distribution of animals, it is perhaps strange that he decided on precisely that distribution which animals could have achieved themselves *without* any direct intervention on his part.

We return to the issue of distribution when we deal with speciation.

What genes say

In every one of my 100 trillion (10^{14}) cells is some nucleic acid made from two helically coiled strands. If any one of those helices were stretched out, it would be about a metre long. It is a very impressive piece of folding. All the folds are contained in structures called chromosomes. Chromosomes are in turn subdivided into the nucleic acid segments which are the units of inheritance – genes. The acid, which is called deoxyribonucleic acid – DNA – is made from just four building blocks, called bases. The DNA acts as the template for proteins. Proteins are made from amino acids. The sequence of bases on the DNA determines the sequence of amino acids in the protein, and that sequence in turn determines the characteristics of the protein. A very minor change in the amino acid sequence can produce a hugely significant change in the protein.

Sperm are constantly produced, in their millions, in my testicles. Although the DNA in each of my cells is (barring mutations) identical, the chance of the DNA in any two of my sperm being the same is minuscule. The same is true of the DNA in my wife's eggs. On three occasions one of those unique sperm has fertilised one of those unique eggs. The result has been three boys, each with a genetic composition which has never before been seen in the entire history of the universe and, unless they are cloned, will never be seen again.

Cells are constantly being bombarded by physical, chemical and radioactive insults. If I go out into the sun, the DNA of

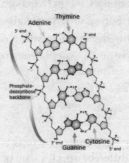

*The basic chemical structure of DNA. Source: Madeleine Price Ball
(GNU Free Documentation Licence).*

my exposed skin is likely to have some of the bases knocked
out of it like a skittle is knocked down at a shooting gallery.
That change will have an effect on the way that cell behaves. It
is likely to be a bad change – most are. It might make the cell
multiply wildly, uninhibited by the usual restraints on cell division, and so be called a cancer. One of the three boys produced
by the meeting of a sperm and an egg did not survive. Although
he looked perfect, perhaps he was the victim of a lethal mutation.

Not all mutations are bad, however. Or at least not all mutations are bad all of the time. Sometimes they are the architects
of dazzling innovation. All in all, the process of normal sexual
reproduction and the phenomenon of mutation are the engines
of breathtaking variety. It is this variety upon which natural
selection gets to work.

A novelty-producing engine is a prerequisite of Darwinian
evolution. There is such a machine. Whether it produces enough
novelty, and at a fast enough rate, is a question to which we

will return. The mere fact that there is such an engine does not in itself question the premises of creationism. What does rock the foundations is the degree of variety that it has produced.

The mutation rate (the rate at which the base skittles are knocked out) can be estimated (with highly contentious degrees of reliability).[30] In the gene that codes for alpha-globin (a protein component of haemoglobin), for instance, there are thought to be about 0.56 changes per base pair per billion years (for changes affecting the protein structure). Where this rate is known, the DNA strands from different species can be used as molecular clocks to determine when species diverged from a common ancestor. Suppose the DNA from species X and species Y differs by four bases, and suppose we know that these DNA lengths change at a rate of about one base per 25 million years. One hundred million years of evolution thus separates the two DNA strands: their common ancestor accordingly lived 50 million years ago.[31] Put another way, barring massive injections of variety from a God-held syringe, you need this much time to explain the observed variety.

The degree of variety is therefore difficult to square with the cornerstone contentions of creationism. There simply is not nearly enough time in the six to ten thousand years from the notional creation for the generation by non-supernatural means of the amount of variation that we see at the genetic level. Of course, if one assumes a constant re-injection of variety from an external creator, one can get round all such difficulties. But that would demand a radical change of tack by the creationists. If creation was concluded in seven days, six to ten thousand years ago, with natural means producing (by a process of degeneration) all subsequent change, you have a big problem.

Genetic variety, then, testifies impressively to the neo-Darwinian mechanism. So too, but even more convincingly, does genetic similarity.

Human and chimpanzee genes are less than 2 per cent different. About 95 per cent of the human genome corresponds directly to that of the chimp. Why? Because they share a fairly recent common ancestor, says the evolutionist. No, says the creationist, this is yet another example of a Rembrandt brush stroke – a favoured blueprint repeated because God made it, God likes it, and it works.

The similarities are not just between humans and higher primates, but between all forms of life. Cytochrome proteins, used in cell respiration and photosynthesis, are coded for by base sequences which are almost identical in widely different organisms. You can barely tell a Nobel Prize winner from an earthworm or a yeast by looking at their cytochrome coding. 'Rembrandt,' says the creationist. 'Relation,' says the Darwinian.

Who is right? Well, perhaps there is no need to choose. But we ought to note that the family tree that you reconstruct by looking at the genome is identical to the one that you get by looking in the rocks. The evidence is beginning to converge very suggestively on Darwinism.

The harder you look at the genome, the worse it gets for the creationist. Five examples make the point.[32]

First, there are families of genes – for instance, those coding for oxygen-carrying proteins in the blood. The further one climbs up the evolutionary tree (or, better the further one clambers along the straggling branches of the evolutionary bush), the more complex one becomes – the more copies of a particular type of gene one tends to have. If you can read this, you have many more copies of the oxygen-carrying protein genes than does a cod, which in turn has twice as many as a liver fluke. Why? The obvious inference is that in the journey from flukedom to humanity via cod-dom, the basic gene has been simply multiplied, and the copies then trimmed and tailored by natural selection to produce the fine-tuning necessary for their host to be able to transport oxygen optimally.

Second, often large sections of DNA, representing several genes, are more or less identical. The most celebrated example involved so-called Hox genes. We will meet them again shortly. They are genetic switches, flipping other genes on and off. The only point for now is that these Hox genes, whether they are in giraffes, gorillas, cress or leeches, are always found in the same order on the chromosome. It is a cut-and-paste job, of a sort entirely compatible with common ancestry.

Third, flanking the clusters of Hox genes, for no apparent functional reason, are other genes. And here's the thing: they too are the same, whether you look in a toad or a toadstool. The inference is the same as before. Both the Hox genes and their flankers have, in some remote common ancestor, been lifted up together in a primeval act of gene duplication and dumped down in the same order in the chromosome of the descendants. Once there, no selective pressure will insist that the order is changed, and so it has not.

Fourth, the Hox genes (as well as other genes) are recruited by different organisms for different purposes. Put a particular Hox gene into *Drosophila* (the fruit fly), and it causes one segment to sprout legs and another to bud wings. But put it in a mouse, and it shapes its brain. This is a common observation in evolutionary biology. Nature has a make-do mentality. It presses ingeniously into service whatever material it has available. As we will see, that observation proves to be the nemesis of the notion of 'irreducible complexity' in the theory of intelligent design. For the moment its significance is that it tends to undermine the creationists' Rembrandt/common design plan plea. They have to use the plea to explain away the identical Hox genes. But if God really is so keen on using Hox genes in that way in fruit flies, why does he not use them that way in mice?

Fifth, there is a lot of genetic redundancy. Whole stretches of DNA ('pseudogenes') just sit there in the cell, never coding for a protein, never switching any other cells on and off, and never doing anything else useful. Indeed, the cell contains about ten times as much DNA as it apparently needs. A lot of this surplus 'junk' DNA is immensely repetitive. It does nothing, and makes tedious reading. Broadly, the more complex the organism, the more junk it has (although plants – perhaps because their chromosomes double up more than animals' – sometimes have more than even sophisticated animals do).

Why is it there? It is forcefully speculated that junk DNA is the off-scouring of evolutionary history: that in the mutation and recombination that produced the raw material of natural selection there was a good deal of incoherent, useless but harmless stuff generated as a by-product. Mutation is generally harmful. One might perhaps expect that even when it produces something useful, it might also produce some rubbish too. If the rubbish does no harm, natural selection will tolerate it, and over the millennia it will simply accumulate in the cell – evidence of a fecund but messy process of novelty generation.

Pseudogenes and junk DNA are an embarrassment to creationists. They have to say that apparently redundant DNA, like the apparently redundant appendix, has an as-yet-undiscovered function.

To sum up, it cannot be denied that we have a lot of subtle things in common with the other organisms on this planet. All those similarities fit with the neo-Darwinian paradigm. It is of course possible that God, in a moment of divine mischief, decided to implant in the genomes of his entirely unrelated creatures misleading suggestions about common ancestry, just as some creationists accuse him of doing in the fossil record. It is possible, too, that he impishly chose to give the impression of random mutation and genetic recombination by loading specifically designed cells with redundant junk. But it somehow does not seem like the sort of thing he would do.

The problem of speciation

The creationists generally concede happily that natural selection results in micro-evolution – the change in characteristics within a species. But, as already noted, they generally dismiss the idea of macro-evolution – that evolution can produce brand-new species. There is one caveat to this. Here it is, expressed in an article on the Answers in Genesis website:

> Poorly informed anti-creationist scoffers occasionally think they will 'floor' creation apologists with examples of 'new species' forming in nature. They are often surprised at the reaction they get from the better informed creationists, namely that the creation model depends heavily on speciation.
>
> It seems clear that some of the groupings above species (for example, genera, and sometimes higher up the hierarchy), are almost certainly linked by common ancestry, that is, are the descendants of one created ancestral population (the created kind, or *baramin*). Virtually all creation theorists assume that Noah did not have with him pairs of dingoes, wolves and coyotes, for example, but a pair of creatures which were ancestral to all these species, and probably to a number of other present-day species representative of the 'dog kind.'
>
> Demonstrating that speciation can happen in nature, especially where it can be shown to have happened rapidly, is thus a positive for creation theorists. A commonly heard objection is that, surely, speciation is evolution, and that the creationists are postulating even more rapid post-Flood evolution than evolutionists do! In reply, it should be pointed out that the difference is all about genetic *information*. The 'big picture' of evolution is that protozoa have become pelicans, palm trees and people. Thus it must have involved processes

which, via natural causes, increased the genetic information in the biosphere.

The creationist assumes that real, substantive increases in information (that is, specifying for an increase in what might be called 'functional complexity') will never arise without intelligent cause. Speciation within the creationist model will therefore be expected to occur in the absence of any increases in the information within the biosphere, and thus can properly be classified as non-evolutionary.[33]

Accordingly, for a creationist, a dingo is a degenerate version (or at least an in-no-way-enhanced version) of the prototypic, generic dog that was on the ark. The Bible merely says that Noah had on the ark two of each 'kind' of animal. A 'kind' is the primordial prototype. Since the whole of creation, before the flood, was declared to be 'very good', creation is not subsequently going to improve. The general direction is down.

The Answers in Genesis website again makes the point well:

After these dogs came off the Ark and the population of dogs increased on the earth, new species of dogs formed as the dog population split up and moved to different places over the earth – but they are all dogs, nonetheless . . . Poodles were developed over time (probably from wolves) like all the other domestic varieties of dogs . . . So we could say that God created the original dogs, and poodles were developed by man from that original – but only using the information that God put there in the first place. So in a sense one could say God made poodles – but only in the sense that God made all the original perfect information for dogs (which existed in the Garden of Eden), which enabled poodles to exist . . . Poodles (like all domestic varieties) are the result of a downward process! They have not just developed from dog genes, but from cursed copies of dog genes! . . . Each time I arrive home and our pet Bichon races to the door to meet me, I am reminded of my sin, that I, in Adam, sinned and ushered in the Fall.[34]

We have already noted that macro-evolution has not been directly observed: we do not live long enough. It is assumed (and it is no more than an assumption) that lots of micro-evolution equals macro-evolution.

There is, however, some evidence which suggests strongly that the assumption is right. Some of that evidence involves islands of various sorts, and three examples make the point.

HAWAIIAN FRUIT FLIES

Hawaii is a very long way from anywhere else. Blown there on a hot wind from somewhere about five million years ago were some tiny fruit flies – *Drosophila*. They found an island bristling with opportunity. Everywhere they looked with their compound eyes there was an unoccupied ecological niche.

Today there are about three thousand species of *Drosophila* in the world. An astonishing eight hundred of them are on the Hawaiian islands, and they have characteristics found nowhere else in the world.

Why so many on Hawaii? Because there was so much less competition there than anywhere else. There was much more room for natural selection to display its creativity. From a single ancestor or a few ancestors, eight hundred species were generated. It is true, too, that small, isolated gene pools, such as there were and are on Hawaii, are far more evolutionarily fecund than big ones. Recessive genes show their hand more often, and promising players more readily catch the eye of natural selection.

The evolutionary paradigm fits the Hawaiian fruit flies very neatly. They do not confound the creationist, but he has to do some embarrassing special pleading – presumably along the lines that God wanted, for some reason known only to him, to favour Hawaii with a dazzling abundance of subtly different fruit flies, while spreading the supply of these fascinating animals very thinly over the rest of the planet.

EAST AFRICAN CICHLIDS

In 1996, geologists conducted a seismic survey of Lake Victoria. The conclusion was dramatic. During the Late Pleistocene period (before about 12,400 years ago), Lake Victoria dried up completely. At best it was a marsh. The geologists speculated that this must have eliminated more or less all the fish. If that were true, how could one explain the presence in the lake of more than five hundred species of brightly coloured cichlids? They postulated that the five hundred must have evolved from a single ancestor – one that had somehow got back into the lake when it refilled, or survived in the marshland slime to become the icthyological Abraham for a whole new dynasty. If it had happened this way, it would have been a dramatic illustration of the power and speed of macroevolution.

Doubt has recently been cast on the 1996 conclusions by 2000 and 2003 papers which used molecular clocks to estimate the period elapsed since the divergence of the Lake Victoria species from their common ancestor.[35] The papers put the date at a hundred to two hundred thousand years ago. While debate continues,[36] the new work gives no comfort at all to creationists. Whether it took twelve thousand or four hundred thousand years, evolution was fairly bowling along.

When there is an isolated population and a mass of vacant niches, it seems that speciation can happen very quickly indeed.

DARWIN'S FINCHES

The story of the Galapagos finches is too well known to need retelling in detail, but briefly it goes like this.

There are only twenty species of land birds on the Galapagos islands. Of these, fourteen are finches. This is a ridiculously high proportion compared to elsewhere. Many whole groups of birds are completely missing, as we should be coming to expect on a remote island. The beaks of the Galapagos finches are beautifully shaped to exploit the various types of food available: they are true, and intensely local, specialists.

Again, the obvious reconstruction is that a small group of mainland finches were caught up in a gust and marooned on the islands. Once there, the isolation meant astonishing opportunity. The world that was the windswept lava and its clinging vegetation was those primordial finches' genetic oyster. It was a black volcanic smorgasbord of unexploited ecological markets. The genes were the entrepreneurs, and natural selection was their driving force.

1. Geospiza magnirostris.
2. Geospiza fortis.
3. Geospiza parvula.
4. Certhidea olivacea.

Darwin's finches, by John Gould. Taken from Voyage of the Beagle, *2nd Ed, 1845.*

Of course it is possible that God simply decided, for reasons of his own, that finches should be grotesquely over-represented on the Galapagos, and other types absent. Perhaps that pattern does glorify him in some obscure way. Perhaps it is yet another example of the quirky exuberance that tells particularly profoundly of God precisely because it confounds our own understanding. None of this can be contradicted.

Can it definitely be said that the Galapagos finches were not descendants of some 'type' finch, lovingly cared for by Noah on the ark, released by him somewhere in the Near East a few thousand years ago, and subsequently speciated by natural selection or other forces in the limited way allowed by Young Earth creationism? Well, 'definitely' is too strong a word for most refined scientific palates, but 'vanishingly improbable' will stand happily in its place. The evidence lies in the DNA; we have dealt with it already.

SPECIATION: A CONTINUING PROBLEM

None of this should be taken to mean that the problem of speciation is solved. It is not. In many ways (and ironically, given the title of Darwin's great book), the origin of species still remains one of the deepest puzzles of biology. But the nature of the puzzle must be clearly understood. It is a puzzle about the exact mechanism.

There is no doubt that speciation happens, and that in some circumstances it can happen really quite fast (in time periods of the order of tens or hundreds of thousands of years). There is no doubt, too, about the basic ingredients you need to produce a new species. To do it best and most quickly in animals like birds and mammals you need an isolated population, reproducing fast using sexual reproduction, set in an environment packed with niches which are either previously unoccupied or occupied by organisms that will not put up much of a fight in the defence of that niche.

The isolation need not be physical. Although the remote island examples play best in the student textbooks, subtler types of isolation work too. They may be behavioural or genetic, for instance. A spitting, gum-chewing trucker may well be behaviourally isolated from a fragrant debutante dressed in Laura Ashley. There are many parallels in the animal world. Other models of speciation work too. Even more rapid speciation may occur where massive, sudden genetic change happens – for example by chromosome doubling in plants and bacteria. Such seismic genetic upheavals will usually produce non-viable monsters; they will very occasionally produce champions.

All that said, the inference that lots of micro-evolution (in the classical Darwinian meaning of that word) produces macro-evolution (in the classical Darwinian meaning of that one) remains just that – an inference. It is a massively strong one and, as we have seen, only a small amount of its strength results from the complete absence of any serious competitor. But some force remains in the objection that stems from Darwin's original observations of artificial selection. He noted not only that artificial selection had signally failed to produce a new species, but that (a) there were limits to the amount of variation that you could produce (you can make rabbits bigger, but you cannot make them as big as cows), and (b) that reproductive 'fitness' tended to diminish in successive generations. It worried him sick. It remains a niggle. But a niggle is not a death blow to an entire, massively evidenced thesis. Still less does it amount, as the creationists tend to suggest, to a self-supporting contrary thesis by itself. It is an unsolved challenge. As an objection, it really has only rhetorical force.

Ancient pain and death

Long before there was any human Adam around to fall, there was death and pain in the world. The earliest evidence of death is of course the very earliest fossils: the cyanobacteria that formed stromatolites nearly 3.5 billion years ago were once alive, and now are not. As soon as the fossil record begins to show animals with hard parts, we see evidence of predation. Many, many organisms are built to kill and to avoid being killed. Some of the most splendid examples of design are of tools for execution. The teeth of *Tyrannosaurus rex* were the way they were so that they could rip the bodies of other dinosaurs.

Stromatolites in Shark Bay, Australia. Photo: Paul Harrison (GNU Free Documentation Licence).

The Bible seems to acknowledge that there is something wrong about predation. We return to the issue in detail later. It acknowledges it by saying that God's original intention was that animals and men should be vegetarian. Of course we know, beyond serious contradiction, that many of the animals existing before the arrival of man were efficient and enthusiastic carnivores.

But even if this were wrong, are we seriously to suppose that a huge brontosaurus, grazing its way through a Jurassic swamp, somehow delicately spared from destruction the insects and other organisms on the plants that it masticated? Of course there was death before man: the planet would be even more dangerously overloaded if there had not been.

Perhaps death by predation is somehow a special case? Perhaps it is willed by God – subject to a special providence? Even if this is right, and one can thereby explain away some of the deaths that comprise the fossil record, we are still left with the fact that our homes are built on and with countless billions of corpses. The shells that make up limestone once contained animals that sensed and crawled and reproduced and then died. There is also incontrovertible evidence of disease many millions of years before man could possibly have bitten into the forbidden fruit.

In 1997, the amateur fossil hunters Cliff and Sandy Linster, digging near Chorteau, Montana, unearthed the skeleton of a dinosaur – a 72-million-year-old female gorgosaurus. Gorgosauruses are not particularly rare, but this one had an interesting quirk. Rattling around inside its skull was a bone ball. It was an extraskeletal osteosarcoma – a bone tumour – which would have encroached on its cerebellum and its brainstem. You can go and look at it in the Children's Museum in Indianapolis.

The gorgosaurus is not the only dinosaur cancer victim we know about. In 2003, the radiologist Bruce Rothschild published his findings of twenty-nine tumours in hadrosaurs – a particularly cancer-prone type of duck-billed dinosaur from the Cretaceous period. They show impressive oncological variety: the tumours include metastatic cancers, haemangiomas, desmoplastic fibromas and osteoblastomas,[37] and an osteosarcoma has recently been reported in a Jurassic camptosaurus, estimated at 150 million years old.

While the nearest relative of *Homo sapiens* was a tiny,

squeaking, shrew-like animal, scurrying around among dinosaur dung, dinosaurs were not only being dismembered alive by other dinosaurs and creaking from osteoarthritis in their joints, but were wasting, staggering and dying under the burden of deeply unkind cancers. It is historically hard to pin the whole thing on Adam or his wife.

Inefficient design

There is a tendency among non-biologically educated Christians with creationist tendencies to assume that the biological world is optimally designed. 'Look at God's astonishing handiwork,' they say. 'We can conclude from it not only that God exists and that he created the world, but also that he is a genius.'

If it were true that the world is indeed optimally designed, that itself would create problems; it would mean that it has been optimally designed for a system in which selfishness and death rule – hardly the sort of thing that reflects well on its designer. The obvious first thought is that if the world is indeed the work of a genius, it is the work of an evil genius. We wrestle with that difficulty later on in this book. But in fact the assumption is not right. There are some serious design flaws. Those flaws tend to contradict the inference that there is a hands-on project manager behind creation.

Take (as we did last week, with new potatoes) a plaice. It lies on the seabed looking up through two eccentrically arranged eyes on the top of its flattened head. It looks as if the whole plaice was originally an ordinary, vertically oriented fish with eyes on the side of its head, and that it has been clumsily flattened, as if with a brick. And indeed, that is more or less what has happened. Its head bones are crazily distorted to allow its eyes to point upwards. Any forensic pathologist looking at an X-ray of a plaice's head would suggest that there had been foul play. If it is the artistry of a designer, it is a designer with strange, wild Cubist leanings.

Flat fish do not have to be like that. If you were designing one from scratch, aiming for elegance and symmetry, you would unquestionably go for something along the lines of a ray.

The natural world abounds with similar examples. The recurrent laryngeal nerves, which innervate the larynx, take a very strange route. Branching off the vagus in the neck, they dive into the chest, where the left recurrent laryngeal weaves around the aorta, and the right around the right subclavian artery, before both head straight back up to the larynx. 'In a giraffe', observes Dawkins, 'this detour must be wasteful indeed.'[38]

Stephen Jay Gould famously went to the zoo. He saw a panda stripping bamboo by passing the stalks between an apparently flexible thumb and its remaining digits. He looked closely, and saw that in addition to the 'thumb', the panda had a further five digits. Did this mean that the panda had evolved an additional true digit, specifically for stripping bamboo?

The answer is no. The bamboo-stripping 'thumb' is no thumb at all. It is a monstrously elongated radial sesamoid bone (the radial sesamoid is normally a small, inconspicuous component of the wrist). In the panda it is massively and usefully deformed, and is equipped with muscles. But they are not new muscles: they are familiar wrist muscles pressed into the service of the monster.[39] The whole thing is, in Michael Ghiselin's words, 'a contraption'. Probably a true thumb would have done a better job at bamboo-stripping than the contraption. The solution is ingenious, but not the sort of thing you would have come up with if you had sat down at the drawing board and said, 'Right, let's design the best mammalian bamboo-exploiting machine that we can.'

Two general themes emerge from any look at imperfections in biological design. First, while aeons of geological time and the rigorous honing of natural selection will often produce a design which (judged by thermodynamic, aerodynamic and other criteria) is optimal, its main interest in a particular organism (if the teleology can be excused for once) is not to make it the best, but to make it better than its competitors. It is therefore content with make-do solutions that give a competitive edge. The flattened skulls of the plaice and the flounder will do. For fish that are trying to exploit the flat-fish niche, they are better than an upright skull. And second, natural selection cleverly assembles workable structures from components that it has already 'designed'. The head of a vertically oriented fish is simply flattened; the panda's radial sesamoid is made longer. The novelty is in the new use of an old thing – nothing radically new has been added to the repertoire; the 'new' tunes are actually cunning reassemblies of old phrases. We see this, too, in the alleged examples of 'intelligent design'. And it is to there that we now return.

The intelligent design hypothesis

'If it could be demonstrated that any complex organ existed, which could not possibly have been formed by numerous, successive, slight modifications,' wrote Charles Darwin in *The Origin of Species*, 'my theory would absolutely break down. But I can find no such case.'[40]

The proponents of the notion of intelligent design say that they can find several such cases, and accordingly that Darwin is hoist by his own petard and Darwinism is in tatters.[41]

We have met the notion already.[42] We saw there that most adherents of ID assume that some evolution occurred by natural selection, or at least that the evidence for this is so strong that there is tactically no point in trying to contradict it.

They say, though, that some things in the natural world are so fantastically complicated that natural selection cannot and never will be able to explain them – that they *necessarily* require an intelligent designer.

There are many things to say about this hypothesis, some of

which have already been said. But here are a few further general points.

The first is that the history of science *is* the history of previously inexplicable things becoming staid, school-textbook orthodoxy. Pick any major scientific milestone you like, in any discipline, to make the point.

The second is that ID assumes an ability to quantify the power of natural selection (in order to say that it is inadequate), which is absurd and contrary to all the evidence. We look briefly at that evidence below, but the position can simply be summarised by saying that we know that natural selection sometimes works, and that it *may* be enough to exclude the need to invoke any other mechanism. But apart from the supremely overconfident Darwinian ultra-fundamentalists, everyone in the field acknowledges that our ability to measure natural selection's transformative power is rudimentary. There is plenty of room for other hypotheses, but *there is absolutely no demonstrated need to invoke them*. Still less can it be demonstrated that any of the other candidates, whether alone or in combination with natural selection, *has* to have the name 'God'. The ID proponents, by claiming that *it can be shown* that an intelligent designer is needed to generate the observed complexity, are claiming to know hugely more about the black boxes of evolution – the genuinely tantalising mysteries – than anyone can seriously claim to know.

The third is that ID is a classic 'God of the gaps' argument. It says, effectively, 'We don't need God to explain 95 per cent of the evidence, but we can't see how the remaining 5 per cent can be explained without him. Therefore he must be the explanation.'

Apologetically, of course, this is exceedingly dangerous. Any competent lawyer instructed on behalf of Christianity would advise against deploying it. For whenever a gap is plugged by new research (and the gaps are being plugged all the time, as we will see), God is nudged nearer and nearer to redundancy.

And each time he is ousted as a necessary explanation, he loses a bit more credibility. That is precisely what has happened and is happening as ID loses ground. If you pin your creed on the earth being the centre of the universe, a short lecture from Copernicus leaves you as an atheist.

It is also an exceedingly odd way to imagine God working. It envisages God wandering round the world, surveying his creation and saying, 'Those bacteria over there – the ones that evolved over the last couple of billion years – they would benefit from flagellae. Natural selection hasn't provided them with flagellae, and so I'm going to give them some. Zap!'

That sort of thinking raises some terrible problems, many of them achingly ethical. What about the gaps that God *has not* chosen to fill? Why does he not intervene in a similarly zapping way to put right some of the real horrors? Why does he not zappingly confer Sudanese children with the immune systems they need to deal with the life-endangering bacteria to which he has so specially and so generously given flagellae?

The bacterial flagellum has long been the jewel in the increasingly dowdy crown of ID. It is undoubtedly an extraordinary piece of engineering. It is a sort of outboard motor, operating at speeds of up to a thousand rotations a minute to propel bacteria along. Its three basic parts – the basal body, the hook and the filament – are built from about forty proteins. The basal body is the engine room, and is embedded in the cell wall. It is made up of a series of rings, and inside is a rod that can rotate through 360 degrees. The rod is attached to a curved protein hook, which in turn is attached to a whip-like structure made from another protein called flagellin. When sodium or hydrogen ions diffuse across the cell wall, the motor whirrs up, the rod spins round and the bacterium is rowed through the soup in which it lives.

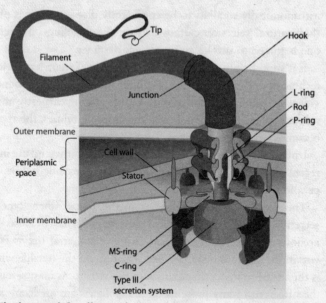

The bacterial flagellum, often cited by proponents of 'Intelligent Design' as an example of 'irreducible complexity'.

The bacterial flagellum is so prized by the ID lobby because, they say, it is a supreme example of 'irreducible complexity'. Each of the components is useless by itself, yet each component is essential to the working of the flagellum. Take one of them away, and the flagellum does not work *at all*. It is not that it continues to work, but works rather less efficiently – you need everything in exactly the position that it is in for the flagellum to work at all. You cannot approach the final flagellum by climbing up the gently rolling hills to the rear of Mount Improbable. Ninety-five per cent of the final thing is no good at all. Natural selection could not find any selective advantage at all in 95 per cent of the final product. And since the chance of all the components being randomly assembled in the only useful way is so astronomically small as to be confidently discounted, it is plain that natural selection cannot explain the flagellum. Therefore one is forced to invoke an intelligent designer.

It is superficially appealing stuff. When backed up by glorious technicolour diagrams of the flagellum and expensively produced videos of white-coated men with beards talking earnestly about repeating flagellin units and terrifying improbabilities, the appeal becomes irresistible to many.

Unfortunately, however, the appeal cannot withstand the most recent research. The jewel in the crown does not dazzle the people who read the scientific journals.[43]

The dazzle started to diminish in the 1990s, when 'type III secretion systems' (T3SSs) were discovered. They are used by noxious bacteria like salmonella to move bacterial toxins from within the cell into a syringe-like structure on the outside which is then used to inject the toxins into the victim. At least seven of the fifteen to twenty proteins of which T3SSs are made are also found in the bacterial flagellum – where they comprise a system called the 'protein export system'. This is a classic homology, like the similarity between a bat wing and a dog's leg: it compellingly suggests descent from a common ancestor. But it also pulls out one of the cornerstone ID arguments – the contention that each of the individual flagellum components is useless by itself.

Dreadfully damaging, too, is the finding that talk of '*the* bacterial flagellum' is simply wrong. The same basic design plan can be seen in all bacterial flagellae, but there are many important variants, suggesting, again, evolution from a common ancestor.

God would be unwise to rest his case for existence or creatorship on the bacterial flagellum – as indeed his self-appointed lawyers found when, relying heavily on the allegedly irreducible complexity of the flagellum, they lost the so-called 'ID trial' in Dover, Pennsylvania, in 2005.

But do the embarrassing failures of ID to demonstrate the

creating hand of God really amount to positive evidence that there is *not* an intelligent designer? Although the exaggerated claims of the ID lobby mean that their failures are likely to be taken that way, it certainly does not. If someone uses an absurd method to try to demonstrate something, their failure is no real comfort to their opponents. Absence of evidence is not evidence of absence.

We have looked already at the evidence that natural selection is to be preferred as a hypothesis to creationism, and the evidence that natural selection can generate and has generated change and variety in the biological world. The evidence for all this is completely overwhelming. Natural selection is certainly a serious candidate for the post of 'designer' – but is it the only candidate? Is there room for anything or anyone else? It is to the evidence about those questions, finally for this chapter, to which we now turn.

How sensitive and powerful is natural selection?

In our discussion of the age of the earth, we were careful to say that the evidence suggested that there was *arguably* enough time for natural selection to have done the job of generating the biological world. We now have to return to the argument implied there.

How much time is enough for natural selection to get from A to B? We cannot say unless and until we know how fast natural selection can work.

This has long been recognised by evolutionists. In the opening lines of his seminal paper, 'A Mathematical Theory of Natural and Artificial Selection', J.B.S. Haldane said:

A satisfactory theory of natural selection must be quantitative. In order to establish the view that natural selection is capable of accounting for the known facts of evolution we must show not only that it can cause a species to change, but that it can cause it to change at a rate which will account for present and past transmutations.[44]

The classical Darwinian model sees mutation as the main, but not the sole, source of the new material to be screened by natural selection for its adaptive promise. While a mutation producing a really spectacular change might result in a colossal one-step leap up one of the precipices on Mount Improbable, it is highly unlikely to do so. It is much more likely to be lethal or profoundly disadvantageous. A mutation *could* have produced an elephant's trunk from a previously flat-nosed proto-elephant in one gigantic, monstrous jump, but, according both to the fossil record and to the statistics behind genetics, it almost certainly did not. Small mutations are much more likely to be the everyday diet of natural selection. The great English biologist Ronald Fisher demonstrated this mathematically. 'The fate of those powerfully selected is quickly settled,' he wrote. 'They do not long contribute to the variance. It is the idlers that make the crowd, and very slight attractions may determine their drift.'[45] These 'slight attractions' were very subtle (generally amounting to selective pressures of 0.1–1 per cent per generation)[46] and yet not only were they detected by natural selection, but they were its main fuel. Do such mutation rates occur naturally? Indeed they do. And they are supplemented by the genetic change that occurs in any sexual reproduction. The contribution of these different sources of genetic change is hard to disentangle, and disentanglement is unnecessary for our present purposes.

Debates about the speed of natural selection generally have the evolution of antibiotic resistance at the top of the bill. And indeed it is spectacular. New and initially effective antibiotics quickly become less than completely effective. What has happened is that among the billions of bacteria subjected to the antibiotic, a few – or perhaps just one – will have a mutation which makes them resistant to the antibiotic. If the mutation is not in itself lethal, it is likely to confer an obvious and very significant advantage to any bacteria exposed to the antibiotic. The ones that have the mutation survive and can reproduce, passing on the mutation to subsequent generations; the ones that do not have it die.

It seems compelling. And in a way it is. But what conclusion does it compel? Only, really, that micro-evolution occurs by natural selection and can occur extremely fast. It is impossible to extrapolate the bacterial lessons safely to many other situations. There are a lot of bacteria, they reproduce extremely quickly and, importantly (and unlike in most other organisms), there is a lot of gene-swapping in bacterial reproduction, making it very hard to trace bacterial lineages. Bacterial antibiotic resistance may be Darwinian natural selection in action, but it is a very special case indeed. Any evolutionist wanting to rest his case on it needs to swathe it so thickly in caveats that its quintessential Darwinian form is barely visible.

Evidence about the speed and power of natural selection outside such special cases is hard to come by. We have seen already that speciation can happen quite quickly (the Lake Victoria cichlids), but one cannot necessarily implicate natural selection in the speciation, and even if one could, one could not confidently say that the Lake Victoria case indicated anything *generally* about the speed with which natural selection works. Indeed, the fossil record suggests that the *general* rate of speciation is far slower than that.

Sometimes it is possible to navigate close to the beating heart of natural selection in the wild. One of the great flagships of evolutionary biology takes us near.

In and outside Oxford there are many brown-lipped snails (*Cepaea nemoralis*). This is not surprising: they are pretty ubiquitous, occurring in many different environments. But the local Oxford populations made them easily accessible, just after World War II, to two zoologists, Philip Sheppard and Arthur Cain.

Their work was to result in some of the clearest evidence we have that natural selection works in natural populations.

The snails' background colour can vary widely; it can be various shades of brown, yellow or pink. They also have dark bands – one, two, three, four or five of them. The colour and banding are controlled by a number of different genes.

The incidence of different types of snails (differently coloured and differently banded) varies between different habitats. But why? Sheppard and Cain conducted a simple and elegant piece of forensic biology, and in doing so saw natural selection dramatically in action.

Thrushes are a significant predator of *C. nemoralis*. They smash them up on anvil stones, leaving the shells lying around as evidence. By looking at the smashed shells, you can see which snails the thrushes had been able to find and kill. By comparing the incidence of the smashed shell types with the incidence of the various types in the surrounding population, you can see just how advantageous it is for a snail to have a particular background colour or a particular configuration of bands. It is found that snail populations vary between habitats: where a particular habitat makes five bands on a yellow background the best camouflage, the incidence of that combination in the population rises. Natural selection appears to be at work.

But, again, what does it all prove? It shows that natural selection is an effective mico-evolutionary engine in those particular circumstances. We cannot export any general lessons outside the Oxfordshire woodlands. It tells us nothing generally applicable about the power of the engine, or the speed of change that it can produce.

Like Haldane, Richard Dawkins is very alert to the importance of being able to demonstrate not just that natural selection is powerful (it very obviously is), but that it is powerful *enough*. To that end he has used 'biomorphs' – images on a computer screen, generated by computerised 'genes', which 'evolve' towards a given shape when the human experimenter picks out the one from a series of 'progeny' that he thinks most resembles the target.[47] Biomorphs are interesting, fun and have their uses. Their main use (and it is of real value) is to challenge our intuitions. They indicate that 'evolution' of a sort can happen counter-intuitively fast. Most are sceptical that they can do much more than that. Life tends to confound the most sophisticated programmers.

Where does all this leave us? The evolutionary biologist Majerus summed it up well. He was talking about the famous example of alleged natural selection of the peppered moth, *Biston betularia*. There are light and dark forms: dark forms predominate in industrial areas where the trees upon which the moths rest have been darkened; light forms predominate in rural areas, where they blend in well with the lichens on the tree trunks. The effect is said to be a result of differential predation by birds – giving a selective advantage in urban areas to the moths carrying the dark gene, and vice versa. The story is complex and controversial, but Majerus's comment stands as a general statement about what biology can and cannot say: '*Biston betularia*', he said, 'shows the footprint of natural selection, but we have not yet seen the feet.'[48]

Not only have we not seen the feet, but the feet travel (as one would expect) at dramatically different paces in different environments. They seem to gallop through small, isolated island populations. They drag in a tired way in big populations in stable places. And perhaps there are places where they do not go at all.

If we cannot see the feet, we cannot see, either, the body of their owner. He might not look like Darwin at all.

There are many genuine and persistent mysteries. Natural selection cannot say so confidently that it is the only possible explanation for the way the world is that all other explanations are necessarily excluded.

CHAPTER 4

Caring and Sharing: The Evolution of Altruism and Community

Does this [reductionist approach] mean that love, generosity, kindness, compassion, honesty and other commendable human characteristics are nothing but the result of conscious, but selfish, survival-oriented neurobiological regulation? Does this deny the possibility of altruism or negate free-will? Does this mean that there is no true love, no sincere friendship, no genuine compassion? That is definitely not the case.

(Antonio Damasio, *Descartes' Error*, 1994)

Sociability, co-operation and apparent altruism are commonplace in nature. Birds flock, ungulates herd, insects build co-operative communities of immense sociological complexity, fish swim in shoals, and humans build cities, trade and go to football matches.

The Naked Mole Rat of East Africa lives in large underground colonies. One of them, the queen, grows to a colossal size and is served by the others, who are celibate workers. The workers' devotion to the colony seems, depending on your point of view, tear-jerkingly admirable or plain pathological. Sometimes they will die for the colony, blocking a tunnel with their own body to stop a snake getting in.[1]

The Naked Mole Rat was the sort of animal that kept Darwin awake at night:

Natural selection cannot possibly produce any modification in any one species exclusively for the good of another species, though throughout nature one species incessantly takes advantage of, and profits by, the structure of another . . . If it could be proved that any part of the structure of any one species had been formed for the exclusive good of another species, it would annihilate my theory, for such could not have been produced through natural selection.[2]

(With the neo-Darwinian emphasis on the individual rather than the species, it is probably legitimate to rewrite this, substituting 'individual' for 'species'.) In fact, he was overstating things. All that would be annihilated would be the premise, held by Dawkins and Dennett but not by Darwin himself, that evolution by natural selection explained absolutely everything about the natural world.

Hard-core evolutionists recognise the danger. Despite some energetic and imaginative efforts over the last hundred years or so to make Darwinism safe from the creeping menace of altruism, the danger persists. Dawkins always looks at his most insecure (which is not very insecure at all) when he is drawn on the issue. We will look at these efforts.

The general view of evolutionary biologists was well stated by William Hamilton: 'As a general rule, a modern biologist seeing an animal doing something to benefit another assumes either that it is being manipulated by the other individual or that it is being subtly selfish.'[3]

The assumption is now supported by a huge literature.[4] It has been transmuted into an axiom. Very broadly, it is assumed that all examples of apparent altruism which have been actively selected for[5] will fall into one of three classes: kin selection, reciprocal altruism, or group selection.

Kin selection is the idea that if X shares enough genetic material with Y, X will help to preserve Y's ability to pass on Y's genetic information (for instance, by saving Y's life). Take an extreme example – a human one, to make the point more obvious. Suppose that X is a childless, vasectomised man. His only relation with reproductive potential is his niece, Y. He sees that she is about to be run over by a bus. He runs into the road at extreme risk to himself and pushes her out of the way. In doing so he is killed himself.

'Kin selection,' says the evolutionist (or he would if X were a seal in comparable circumstances: everyone admits that humans are rather odd). Y is the only relevant vehicle for X's genes. X's genes somehow compel him to override his normal self-preserving instincts for the longer-term benefit of ensuring the survival of the genes he shares with Y.

The great evolutionist Haldane, doodling on a napkin in a pub, concluded, looking up from his calculations, 'I'll gladly give my life for two brothers or four cousins.' (In fact, he got his mathematics wrong: it should have been eight cousins, and was corrected in later textbooks.) The mathematics works: it would predict, for instance, a ratio of three female worker ants to one male. And that is what you see.

Kin selection is a curiously anthropomorphic idea. It implies some sort of dialogue between the genes and the body that bears them. 'Save our clones in that body over there,' they whisper. 'It doesn't matter about us in this one. Jump in front of that bus. It'll be better in the long run. Not for you, of course – you'll be dead. But for our clones. And you, after all, only exist to carry us around. We are the whole point of you.'

It is strange that anyone or anything ever finds that sort of speech at all persuasive. It is deeply strange that anyone or anything ever finds it so completely persuasive that they kill themselves – either actually, by running metaphorically into a road, or reproductively, by sacrificing to another their own chance of reproducing.

We have no idea how these suicidal messages are passed from the genes to the brain, or indeed if they are. We have no idea how the principal canon of natural selection ('Survive') is not only redefined in the organism to something rather different ('Help your shared genes survive'), but also completely over-ridden ('Die, that our clones might live'). Even if it makes perfect mathematical sense on the back of Haldane's napkin, how on earth did natural selection ever allow organisms, programmed for individual, selfish survival, to test Haldane's equations?

Kin selection, which originally seemed so promising, has recently been in decline. The theory's father, E.O. Wilson, now embarrassed at the claims he originally made for it, has published the nearest thing to a full recantation that we are likely to see in the biological world.[6] The theory worked best for the social insects: there are now serious doubts about whether it works (or works as simply as it was originally thought to do, unassisted by other principles) even there.

While kin selection has been in decline, reciprocal altruism has been in the ascendant. It is an important, powerful and revolutionary idea. Richard Alexander said that anyone who believed in the adequacy of the Darwinian paradigm before the advent of the theory of reciprocal altruism was believing the right thing only by accident.[7] It is based on the principle, 'You scratch my back, I'll scratch yours.'

Costa Rican vampire bats that go more than sixty hours without a blood meal are at risk of starvation. When they do feed, though, they generally get more than they need. There are two options: they can regurgitate the surplus blood onto the ground, or they can regurgitate it into the mouth of another bat. Often they opt to share it. The recipient bat obviously benefits: it will not have to fly out so soon to feed again. But the donating bat also benefits, because only donors become donees. It is a classical, simple example of mutual back-scratching.[8]

On many coral reefs you will find 'cleaning stations'. Big fish come to have their external parasites picked off by a whole array of smaller fish and shrimps, many of whom have particular livery – a sort of cleaners' uniform – to mark them out. The cleaners benefit from the food; the cleaned benefit by being relieved of their parasite burden. The cleaners do not get eaten because their services, and the continuing services of cleaners, are worth more to the big fish than the cleaners would be worth as a meal.

Back-scratching systems are quite intellectually demanding. You need a fairly big brain to remember who has scratched your back. If back-scratching is a good thing (in the sense that it confers a selective advantage), then natural selection will tend to favour more back-scratching, and more sophisticated forms of back scratching. To favour co-operation and sociability is accordingly to favour bigger brains. And that is exactly what we see. There is a close correlation between brain size and the size of social groups in both primates and carnivores. Applying that correlation to humans suggests that the optimal group size for us is 150 – making it unsurprising that cities are deeply dysfunctional places.[9]

If you have a big enough brain, you can take advantage of increasingly exotic permutations of the basic mutual back-scratching model. Game theory has been pressed interestingly and effectively into service to analyse the permutations. Any reciprocal altruism scenario can be regarded as an example of the famous 'Prisoner's Dilemma' – broadly any situation where X is tempted to do something (such as retain all its food for itself), but knows that it would be unfortunate if every other member of the group did the same thing (because then X would never get any food from any other member).

The ideal situation for the group and the individuals within it will be when the strategy of each player in the notional game is an optimal response to the strategies of the other players – and accordingly no player has any incentive to deviate from their own strategy. This is described as the 'Nash equilibrium' – after the father of game theory, the Princeton mathematician John Nash. Accordingly, one would expect natural selection to tune animal instincts so that the Nash equilibrium is achieved.

Is that what we see happening in the natural world? It is difficult to say. The approach taken by convinced Darwinians assumes so devoutly the truth of the reciprocal altruism thesis (so much being staked on it) that the analysis tends to look like this: Does that group exhibit a Nash equilibrium? If yes: that is exactly what we would expect; our analysis is vindicated. If no: natural selection is pushing it in that direction; it will get there in time, although there are of course blips on the way.

A huge amount of ingenuity and ink has been used to squeeze the whole of animal behaviour into the boxes of kin selection or reciprocal altruism. Reciprocal altruism is immensely more elastic than kin selection (you can always find a game theorist of sufficient cleverness to tell you that your chimps or cheetahs are playing some game or other) and correspondingly less capable of contradiction (there is nothing so simple and so potentially embarrassing as those figures on the napkin).

Reciprocal altruism is fecund. It has given birth to some other ideas which are more clever and interesting than they are seriously useful. One is worth mentioning because it indicates how, if you think hard enough, you can see natural selection as the agent for anything that you want it to be responsible for. The example is a theory that notes the importance of reputation in determining behaviour. This does not apply only to human or other very 'high' animal behaviour: it is important for the big, parasitised fish to have a reputation for not eating its cleaners. But it is well demonstrated in humans. Humans seem to be very good at distinguishing (by facial appearance and nuances in the voice) between real and faked altruism. If altruism is valued, and status (and accordingly reproductive success) is enhanced by being *really* altruistic, natural selection might well produce a genuinely altruistic individual – or, more strictly, a person who is wholly unconscious that he is really acting selfishly. All his facial and vocal cues will beam out 'sincere altruism'. A person who is genuinely self-deceived will defeat a lie-detector.

If behaviour really cannot be made to fit into reciprocal altruism or kin selection, there is another Darwinist option – group selection.[10] This is the idea that natural selection can work at the level not merely of the individual, but also of the group: co-operative groups have a selective advantage over non-cooperative ones. It is very much the poor relative of the other two theories, particularly to hard-core biologists, who have tended to regard it as the disreputable province of anthropologists and sociologists, whom they do not see as proper scientists.

It is easy to see the reason for their suspicion of group selection, particularly if they are in the ultra-orthodox Darwinian camp. If natural selection is all and only about the survival of genes (or, as we will see, other selfish replicators), evidence of it working at a level other than the individual is the thin end of a very dangerous wedge. Matt Ridley expresses the old orthodoxy well. He notes that anthropologists talk all the time in terms of group selection, 'mostly in blithe ignorance of the fact that biologists have thoroughly undermined the whole logic of group selection. It is now an edifice without foundation.'[11]

Ridley wrote that in 1996. Since then group selection has undergone something of a renaissance and a rehabilitation. One can now, even at a zoological conference, use the words 'group selection' without necessarily losing your career. Group selection seems intuitively right and, particularly in carnivores and primates, is acquiring a fairly strong empirical foundation.

The main objection to group selection is really that it is yet another example of rather complex reciprocal altruism. There is no real self-sacrifice on behalf of the group: the individual stays within the group and acts as he does because it is in his own best interests to do so. Take the example of a professional football team. X and Y are both players. If X scores a goal, he will get an additional £1,000. Similarly for Y. If the team wins, all the players get an additional £500 each. X gets the ball. From his position he stands a 60 per cent chance of scoring a goal. If he passes the ball to Y, however, Y has a 70 per cent chance of scoring. If either scores, the team will win. If neither scores, the team will lose. X passes the ball to Y, Y scores, claiming his £1,000 plus the £500 that everyone on the team gets for winning. X just gets the £500. He probably would have got £1,500 had it not been for the apparently altruistic act of allowing Y to score (altruistic to Y personally and altruistic on a group basis to the whole team). X benefits from the £500 (which he had a higher chance of getting if Y took the shot). He also benefits, no doubt, from the enhanced status within the group that his 'altruistic' reputation gives him.

Almost without exception, the opponents of group selection said, 'Look hard at the alleged group selection, and you see selfishness or kin selection beneath.' Those ant colonies, which might seem to produce prime examples of group selection, are (if you look at the amount of shared DNA within them) just big families. It is the same for a pack of African wild dogs or a troupe of meerkats. Some big conglomerations of animals might live together and die together – in that limited respect the group is indeed a unit on which natural selection acts – but they do so because each individual is better off that way. There is safety *for the individual* in numbers. A huge shoal of sardines is more likely to be hunted and swallowed by a whale than an individual fish: in that sense there is a disadvantage to being sociable. But the chance of the *individual* dying is less in a huge crowd than if it roamed the oceans alone.

We need not look in any more detail at the argument about whether group selection is real. We ought to observe that even if it is, it is hardly more *morally* defensible than any other kind of apparent altruism. If you are not in the group that is co-operating 'altruistically' and effectively, you would not think the individual sacrifices made within that group to be particularly nice. The unpleasant result of the other two models is murder; the unpleasant result of this one is genocide.[12]

What everyone is agreed about is that neither kin selection, nor reciprocal altruism, nor group selection is an adequate explanation for absolutely all behaviour. There is one mammal that just will not fit, or at least fit all of the time, into any of the boxes.

Matt Ridley, spurning the group selectors again, and putting far too high the case for the almost-all-explaining power of evolutionary theories of altruism, says this:

There is simply no good example, to this day, of an animal or plant that has been found to practise group selection unless in a close or closely related family – except in the temporary and passing condition of new-colony formation in the desert seed harvester ant. Bees risk their lives to defend the hive, not because they wish the hive itself to survive, but because they wish the genes they share with their many sisters in the hive to survive. Their courage is gene-selfish.

In recent years, however, a note of doubt has crept into the certainty with which some biologists trot through this argument. They do not doubt its central truth, but they think they may have found an exception to it, a species in which the unlikely conditions apply that could allow groups of co-operators to have such a large advantage over groups of selfish individuals that they could drive the selfish groups extinct before being infected by them. The exception is, of course, the human being.[13]

Human beings go in for evolutionarily ridiculous altruism. They die not only for non-relatives, but for enemies. Sometimes whole groups sacrifice themselves, blowing to pieces any explanation based on group selection. If man is just another creature of natural selection, it is all very odd and very embarrassing.

A fig-leaf has been produced to cover some of the shame. It is the pseudo-science of memetics. Memes, like genes, are supposed to be selfish, self-replicating units. A tune, a method of making something, or an idea might be a meme. They are invisible to the neuroanatomists and the biochemists. In fact, they are invisible. They are supposed to be transmitted horizontally: if religion is meme-based, for instance, I suppose that priests spray memes all over their congregations, somehow infecting them.

Natural selection is supposed to work on memes like it works on genes. If they exist at all, they are presumed to exist only in humans – yet another odd facet of human uniqueness. If they ooze in some way out of consciousness, why do bonobos not have them? Even though the very idea of memes is so amorphous that it is almost impossible to define them linguistically, and it is wholly impossible to see or otherwise trace them, they apparently, according to their advocates, have utterly awesome power. They repeatedly and catastrophically trump genes (the genes which, in the rest of the evolutionists' talk and research, trump everything else, even the individual). They make men submit themselves and their children to torture and death, and massive groups to live in poverty, chastity and self-abasement. If genes are selfish replicators, and memes are selfish replicators, selfishness is truly a house divided, and it is surprising that it has not collapsed completely.

Quite apart from all this, there are very good technical reasons to think that memes are the stuff of fairy stories. The main one is that, as was recognised long ago by Ronald Fisher, natural selection needs a Mendelian form of inheritance to be effective. Memetic change is palpably non-Mendelian: it is Lamarckian. (Lamarck proposed the inheritance of acquired characteristics: a giraffe, by stretching upwards, acquires during its lifetime a lengthened neck. It passes that to its offspring. The idea is anathema to modern genetics. While there may – highly controversially – be some extremely rare and wholly unimportant examples of it occurring in, e.g., bacteria, it can safely be assumed for present purposes that it does not happen.)

Stephen Jay Gould wrote, 'Evolutionists have long understood that Darwinism cannot operate effectively in systems of Lamarckian inheritance – for Lamarckian change has such a clear direction, and permits evolution to proceed so rapidly, that the much slower process of natural selection shrinks to insignificance before the Lamarckian juggernaut.'[14]

The extreme examples of altruism that we have mentioned often, but by no means always, occur in the context of religious belief. Will religion, which in its battle against selfishness seems to be a bitter opponent of Darwinian selfishness, turn out to be a child of natural selection after all – a sibling of the owl's claw, the mosquito's proboscis and the AIDS virus? We look briefly in the next chapter at what the evolutionists say about religion.

Before moving there, however, we should take stock of where the curious issues of sociability, co-operation and altruism leave us.

The theistic evolutionists, almost to a man, are over-deferential to the Darwinians on these issues. Perhaps the ones with a biological background are steeped so thoroughly in Darwinian orthodoxy that rebellion against its axioms is intellectually or psychologically impossible. Perhaps they are concerned about being labelled creationists (a perfectly legitimate concern in itself). And perhaps the ones with a theological background do not sufficiently appreciate the ubiquity of co-operation and apparent altruism in the natural world.

Darwin expressly recognised that altruism was a potential Achilles heel. The attempts to defend it are ingenious but profoundly unconvincing. Memetics in particular are laughable – the very last and wholly inadequate refuge of the desperate Darwinist. When it comes to altruism and co-operation, our Darwinian emperors may have no clothes at all.

It is almost always forgotten that *to provide an explanation for something is not to give an account of its origins*. It is one thing to say that blood-sharing benefits vampire bats; it is quite another to say how the sharing started in the first place. Once apparent altruism is seeded, it is easy to understand how, if it confers a benefit, it will spring up, flourish and be subject to the ordinary forces of natural selection. But how did natural selection, for whom selfishness is the ruling canon, ever allow the blood-sharing seed to exist or to become established? Natural selection stalks around animal and plant communities stamping on apparent selflessness unless and until the selflessness can credibly declare that it is really selfishness in disguise. And natural selection is an extremely efficient stamper.

In man, there has been a massive rebellion against the dictates of natural selection, and natural selection failed abjectly to suppress it. We need not cite Mother Teresa: Richard Dawkins will do. 'We, alone on earth,' he wrote in *The Selfish Gene*, 'can rebel against the tyranny of the selfish replicators.'[15] And, like all decent people, he believes that there is a duty to rebel.

For good Darwinian reasons, evolution gave us a brain whose size increased to the point where it became capable of understanding its own provenance, of deploring the moral implications and of fighting against them . . . So, the Devil's Chaplain might conclude, Stand tall, Bipedal Ape. The shark may outswim you, the cheetah outrun you, the swift outfly you, the redwood outlast you. But you have the biggest gifts of all: the gift of understanding the ruthlessly cruel process that gave us all existence; the gift of revulsion against its implications.[16]

Natural selection, in other words, has produced a Frankenstein that can and must frustrate its parent's diabolical ways. It is uncharacteristically remiss of natural selection.

Another general warning – again, almost always forgotten: *the fact that it is possible to show that an apparently altruistic act confers an advantage does not in itself prove that the act is not altruistic.* Suppose a soldier rushes out into no-man's-land under heavy fire to rescue a wounded comrade. Suppose that the rescuer expected to die in the attempt. His action has to be characterised as truly altruistic, in just the way that worried Darwin sick. In fact, he survives. He gets his country's highest award for gallantry and after the war, on the basis of his celebrity, has the pick of the girls and a lucrative career in business. He has benefited hugely from his altruism, but the benefits were not the reason for it. If the soldier were a dolphin instead of a human, an evolutionist, writing up the scenario in a scientific paper, would point to the benefit and say, entirely wrongly, that this was yet another example of selfishness being draped in ordinary, naturally selective selflessness.

What you see in the natural world depends very much on the lens through which you look. If you come to it expecting nothing but selfishness, that is what you see. So you can and you will explain apparent selflessness as selfishness. Darwin has got so far into us that we no longer see that as perverse.

The fact remains, however, that from the very earliest times the natural world has had in it a vast amount of community. The history of life – the most basic evolutionary observation – is the history of growing complexity. Life was not only single-celled for long. We quickly see conglomeration and, with it, co-operation – co-operation between parts of cells, between cells and between individuals. The drive towards complexity can easily be expounded as a drive towards co-operation. Darwinists are very ready to describe the increasing brain size that we see in evolutionary time as an adaptation that confers a selective advantage on the individual. The assumption is quickly and irrationally made that the advantage is the *reason* for the selection of a randomly enlarged brain and survival of the larger brain. But one might just as well say, with just as much supporting evidence, that the larger brain permitted more co-operation and more community, and was selected for that reason. Yes, of course the concomitant co-operation and community will benefit the individual too, but that does not mean (witness the example of the valiant soldier who later benefits from his altruism) that the main engine of the change was not a principle of selflessness and sociability.[17, 18]

We see community and sociability in the fossil record: cells cluster together, coral reefs form, fish shoal, dinosaurs graze together. We cannot, of course, infer even apparent altruism from this. We need to look at living animals for that. All we can say is that wherever we look in the world – from ants to Nobel Prize winners – we see examples of apparent altruism. In terms of geographical distribution, it is just as ubiquitous as selfishness. In terms of temporal distribution, there is no reason at all to suppose that a similar pattern did not exist in the animal communities represented in the fossil record. Yet the scientific orthodoxy says that selfishness is the solution – the engine of it all – and this apparent altruism is a problem that has to be explained by selfishness. But what if selflessness, properly examined, is not selfishness at all? What if the blindingly obvious answer is the real one: that the apparent selflessness is real? What if one of the main forces driving the generation of the natural world is selflessness? Then it begins to be possible to go for happy walks in the countryside with the bird book again.

We should be clear what we are saying and what we are not saying here.

We are not saying that organisms act altruistically or co-operatively because their conscious intention is to be altruistic or co-operative. That would be absurd anthropomorphism, and it is quite unnecessary for this thesis. The Darwinians, of course, are actually guilty of this anthropomorphism themselves. In asserting that the apparent altruism is not altruism at all, they generally mean that the organism has no such intentionality (which I agree), and that there is a benefit from the apparently altruistic act (which I also agree). They rely on the absence of intentionality – so insisting that intentionality is somehow important. Suppose there is a God who has set the whole natural world running. Suppose that he injected into it (because it pleases him, and because it reflects his nature) a tendency to act sociably, co-operatively and altruistically. And suppose, as is very often the case, that to behave in that way confers a benefit. It still makes sense to describe the unconsciously altruistic acts of the creatures as altruistic. Someone who coughs in his sleep is still accurately described as coughing. But nothing much turns on this.

We are not abandoning natural selection as a force. Far from it. It is perfectly clear that natural selection has contributed in a very significant way to the shape of the world as we see it. Moreover, a good deal of that contribution appears to have been in the morally repugnant way against which Darwin, Dawkins and all decent people rail – the way that involves the ruthless suppression of the weak. However, a process of natural selection might also have been at work instilling into the natural world a mode of being that is selfless and genuinely community based. All the Darwinian explanations for 'apparent' altruism indeed say that this is what happened and happens, but assert that the altruism must be unreal. It is impossible to see, though, how selfish natural selection could have allowed even apparent altruism to start in the first place. Perhaps there was a good force seeding it and inhibiting the usually unswerving efficiency of the selfish stamper.

There are some tentative but exciting empirical suggestions that demonstrably real, unfeigned altruism might be genuinely good for you – and might confer the sort of survival benefit that traditional Darwinian natural selection would recognise and select for. In a prospective study of mortality among older adults, it was found that in the given year study period, providing emotional support to a spouse and providing active, tea-making type support to a social network were independently associated with a 30 to 60 per cent reduction in mortality risk. These effects could not be accounted for by other measures of the physical or mental health of the participants, by their personality, or by other interpersonal variables. The title of the paper in which the results were published summarises it well: 'Providing support may be more beneficial than receiving it'.[19] These results have been replicated in a different, seven-year study of a nationally representative sample of retired people. The participants identified as 'caregivers' lived longer than the takers.[20] In a cancer self-help group, the people who gave more – made the tea, spent more time listening than being listened to, and sympathising rather than demanding sympathy – had longer survival times. Real, sacrificial giving and sharing might be linked inextricably to our capacity to flourish. And if for us at a conscious level, why not for other animals at an unconscious one, or at whatever level of consciousness they can manage?[21]

Once community and altruism are established, they become an engine themselves, so providing, exhilaratingly, another candidate to compete against 'nasty' natural selection for the title of variety generator. Since we can measure accurately the power of neither nasty natural selection nor altruism and community, both must remain in the frame. Probably the better view is that both contributed; that they have been competing head to head over the ages. Metaphysically and intuitively, it is the competition you would expect: selfishness against selflessness. And surely it explains the strange mix that we see. We admire the lion. We say that it is beautiful. Quite a lot of its beauty is directly attributable to the fact that it is designed as a killing machine. At a very deep level we dislike the idea of killing. We need the sort of competition we are now postulating to explain the sort of ambiguity that taxes every thoughtful person with a pair of binoculars and a sprinkling of ecology. It got its canines from the dark and its quintessential majesty from the light.

Which has had the upper hand might seem to depend on your psychology, the weather, and your state of digestion. Do we live in a basically good world with some nasty bits in it? Or do we live in a basically nasty world with some bits of good in it? Objectively, however, that cannot be the case. One of the two competing forces must have been more powerful than the other; must have been the primary determinant of the direction and basic shape of nature. Oxford is grey today, the children are screaming downstairs, and the newspaper tells of horrors. Nonetheless, I know which option I would go for.

If competition has a competitor, if selfishness might sometimes be elbowed out of the way by altruism, if there is a battle on for peace at the heart of nature, who knows where we might stop? If the counter-intuitive clevernesses designed to maintain the monopoly of traditional Darwinism might sometimes fail – if it might occasionally be true that apparent altruism is not downright selfishness – all sorts of exciting thoughts are possible. Now that we have our foot in the door, let's press the advantage a little.

Darwinism deploys paradox in another suspicious and ingenious way – to explain absurd exuberance. Not for the Darwinian ultras the implicit supernaturalism of Nabokov the entomologist, who commented that moth mimicry was quite unnecessarily good. The peacock's tail is an embarrassment for Darwin. The wattles of the Temminck's tragopan are much too artistic. The bower bird, as he builds and decorates with artefacts a colossal palace for the hoped-for mate, is taking far too much trouble. In each case something far less elaborate would surely have done.

Darwinism's basic model of the world is one of prudent, black-suited, tight-lipped Presbyterianism, in which natural selection forces each organism to conduct a rigorous thermodynamic audit of itself. Each organism will be allowed to use enough energy and to take the risks statistically necessary to maximise the chances of its genes being reflected in the next generation. That energy, those risks, and no more. It makes a lot of sense. The trouble is that it is confounded by the real world.

Just think what the audit would say about the peacock. There would be lots of stern tut-tutting, at least at the start. But yet, the Darwinists say, once you have worked through the sums, the bottom line looks all right. Yes, there is a colossal metabolic cost of producing and maintaining that tail; yes, lugging it around does make the bird more vulnerable to predators. But for the individual peacock it is worth it precisely *because* (and here comes the ingenuity) it is disadvantageous. The peahen is supposed to look at the peacock with the most splendid tail and say, 'If he can survive, thrive and display while shouldering the burden of all that finery, he must have excellent genes.' Hence she selects him. Note that it has not been proved that this is the case. Nobody has done the arithmetic. In our present state of knowledge, it is impossible arithmetic to do. This is Alice in Ecological Wonderland. The wholly bizarre presumption is necessary in order to keep intact the Darwinian monopoly on explanation. If you can make presumptions like that you can magic away, with a whisk of your paradoxical wand, all uncomfortable anomalies.

By now we should be used to asking about origins. One can imagine how, once the peacock gets his tail, the Darwinian explanation might work to keep the tail there, and keep the tail splendid. But how on earth did Darwin allow the tail to get there in the first place? Would he not have trimmed its genes to sensible, workmanlike proportions when they first started having ridiculous aesthetic aspirations?

Perhaps, just perhaps, there is another force operating alongside natural selection: a force that is an ally of real community and real altruism; a force that rejoices in beauty for its own sake.

CHAPTER 5

The Biology of Awe:
The Evolution of Religion

Knowing that we are products of Darwinian evolution, we should ask what pressure or pressures exerted by natural selection originally favoured the impulse to religion.

(Richard Dawkins, *The God Delusion*)

We can be short. Religion exists, and the ultra-Darwinians do not like it. They dislike the content of religion, its effects and (most profoundly) the fact that it exists at all. A world without religion (as, indeed, a world without human beings and their quirks) would be much neater, would be far easier to squeeze into the constructs of neo-Darwinism. And neatness is almost everything. If there are exceptions to the supposedly universal explanatory power of Darwinian natural selection, you have to learn to live with complexity and uncertainty, and that is uncomfortable as well as impious. As we have noted already, religion threatens to ruin the equations. It causes people to do some outrageously non-Darwinian things.

When the ultras get worried, they start shouting, in the hope that it will pass for argument; in the hope that the sound, volume and emotional heat generated will obscure the fact that their position does not bear calm analysis. Hence Dawkins's splendid, flawed, but rightly bestselling book *The God Delusion*, the manifesto of the New Atheism.[1] It is a book blissfully unencumbered by doubt or nuance. Everything is simple for him, at least in principle. 'Historically, religion aspired to *explain* our own existence and the nature of the universe in which we find ourselves. In this role it is now completely superseded by science.' Completely? Is there nothing to discuss?

He is at his buccaneering best when dealing with the creationists. But it is an unequal contest. It is not quite sporting. It is like hunting dairy cows with a heat-seeking missile. It is not big, it is not clever, but I am afraid that it is quite funny.

He is, of course, right about many things. He is right to remind us, for instance, that the ability of an idea to inspire or console is no index of its truth or falsehood. And so, entertained by his regular diatribes and nodding at his wisdom, we easily forget that the book is a portfolio of assertions, not of argument. He lulls our critical faculties to sleep, and many fall into the very error that he has just warned us about. He tells us that religion has done bad things, and invites us to conclude that its basic propositions are therefore untrue. He tells us that science (and Darwinian natural selection in particular) can explain the world, but offers nothing approaching a convincing explanation of the bizarre phenomenon of religion itself.

He retreats into memetics, which we have already met and giggled at. Here he is on memes:

> One respect in which [memes] are not like genes is that there is nothing obviously corresponding to chromosomes or loci or alleles or sexual recombination. The meme pool is less structured and less organized than the gene pool. Nevertheless, it is not obviously silly to speak of a meme pool, in which particular memes might have a 'frequency' which can change as a consequence of competitive interactions with alternative memes.[2]

On this he builds a massive and superficially appealing superstructure that purports to give an entirely naturalistic explanation for the existence and nature of religion. But read the

passage again. It is beyond parody. What he is covertly acknowledging is that there is no evidence whatever for the existence
of memes. His exposition is a detailed description of the finer
points of the history and design of the brocade on the non-
existent clothes of that emperor. The description is even more
detailed in the recent book by his henchman Daniel Dennett,
Breaking the Spell: Religion as a Natural Phenomenon.[3] To
devote two long books to what one sees as a laughable delusion begins to look like worry.

One cannot judge the scientific worth of a theory by the best-
seller lists. Dawkins and Dennett, although they have many lay
disciples, have few serious scientific fellows. And in particular
very few workers in the field of the evolution of religion agree
with the Dawkins/Dennett viral contagion model – a model that
looks to have been built far more by deep-seated personal
animosity than by neo-Darwinian orthodoxy, and not at all by
empiricism.

There are some serious researchers in the area, though, and
many of them think that there may be evolutionary explanations for religion.[4]

There is growing evidence that religious belief is innate –
something that comes with the baggage of humanity. Young
children seem to start religious (or at least with a hyperactive
belief in the action of agents who are responsible for doing
things in the world), and gradually get less so. Far from being
learned, then, as Dawkins would have it, religion seems to be
progressively *unlearned.*[5] It is primordial, and then we often
lose it. We look again at the significance of that observation
when we examine just what the Judaeo-Christian tradition means
when it talks about the fall.

But this does not explain why or how belief arose in the first
place: how that Hypersensitive Agent Detection Device[6] in the
baby's brain got there.

There are various speculations. It is a consequence of a spandrel, thought Stephen Jay Gould. A spandrel is an evolutionary by-product of a characteristic specifically selected for, which just lies around in the genome, sometimes making itself heard.

> The human brain must be bursting with spandrels that are essential to human nature and vital to our self-understanding but that arose as non-adaptations, and are therefore outside the compass of evolutionary psychology, or of any other ultra-Darwinian theory. The brain did not enlarge by natural selection so that we would be able to read and write. Even such an eminently functional and universal institution as religion arose largely as a spandrel if we accept Freud's old and sensible argument that humans invented religious belief largely to accommodate the most terrifying fact that our large brains forced us to acknowledge: the inevitability of personal mortality. We can scarcely argue that the brain got large so that we would know we must die.[7]

Indeed, that cannot be argued. But there are grave difficulties with Freud's/Gould's position. Why should something as ubiquitous, as inevitable and as apparently natural as mortality ever have been perceived in the first place as a problem requiring any kind of solution, let alone a solution with as high a cost as religion? Why should those early men, recognising with the consciousness bequeathed to them by their big brains, come to think that death was any more noxious than sleep? Yes, there must be an evolutionary benefit in making death something to be avoided for as long as possible (or as long as you are capable of passing on your genes), but when it happens, as it must, why worry? 'Does a fish complain of the sea for being wet?' asked C.S. Lewis. If we are purely natural creatures, why are we not happy to imagine ourselves and our loved ones, at least in our reproductive senescence, lying down and returning to the dust?

Other adaptationist solutions have invoked group selection, and that does seem a more promising avenue. One can see that religion might help groups to cohere and co-operate. The threat of punishment in an afterlife might work like a patrolling policeman, discouraging behaviour inimical to the group's success and encouraging participation in ways helpful to the group.[8] We have seen already, in discussing altruism, that insincerity is easily detected, and accordingly religious sincerity (as opposed to mere lip service) might itself confer an advantage.[9]

There may be some truth in these suggestions. They may well explain how religion, once seeded in a society, might be transmitted through it and maintained within it. But, just as we noted in looking at the purported evolutionary explanations of altruism, that is a long way from explaining how the idea got seeded there in the first place (when one would expect natural selection to deal brutally with the seed). It is hard to see, too, why natural selection would tolerate the more extreme forms of apparently anti-Darwinian behaviour seen in many religions (such as self-immolation and celibacy). Even if there were (as there is not) a perfectly good naturalistic explanation for the origin of religion, so what? It would not mean that other explanations are impossible. And it would not begin to tell us anything at all about the truth of its contents.

Ian Tattersall writes in *Becoming Human*[10] about a limestone cliff face near Les Eyzies de Tayac, in south-western France. A fissure, the course of an ancient underground stream, dives deep into the rock. About a hundred and fifty yards along, the wall suddenly buds. It is decorated with over three hundred beautifully observed and executed engravings of wild mammals. They are about thirteen thousand years old, and were made at the end of the last Ice Age. There are many such engravings across the world, but there is something special about these. You can walk into the cave only because its floor has very recently been dug out. At the time that the walls were inscribed, the cave was in places less than two feet high. It would have been in complete darkness until the artists brought fire in with them. It would have taken the best part of an hour to belly-crawl through the dark to this place. It is on the way to nowhere. Almost anywhere else would have been more accessible. Why crawl there?[11] It was presumably a votive journey of some sort. Men have been doing such journeys, for no reason that Darwin can begin to speculate coherently about, ever since men became men. In a way, every journey that he has ever made is a similar votive crawl.

CHAPTER 6

The Tangled Book:
The Creation Accounts in Genesis

What person of intelligence, I ask, will consider as a reasonable statement that the first and the second and the third day, in which there are said to be both morning and evening, existed without sun and moon and stars, while the first day was even without a heaven? ... I do not think anyone will doubt that these are figurative expressions which indicate certain mysteries through a semblance of history.

(Origen, c. AD 185 – c. 254, *First Principles*)

The Scriptures do not need to be interpreted. God is able to say exactly what he means.

(Henry Morris and John Whitcomb, *The Genesis Flood: The Biblical Record and its Scientific Implications*)[1]

We only interpret the Word of God by the Word of God when we interpret the Bible by science.

(Charles Hodge, 'The Bible in Science', *New York Observer*, 26 March 1963)

Among the many unholy agreements of Richard Dawkins and the Young Earth creationists, the one that is most basic, most disappointing and most corrosive is their radical misunderstanding and underestimation of the book of Genesis.

On a quick reading it seems like a simple book, rather artlessly cobbled together by an amateurish editor. If you read it that way without taking it seriously (Dawkins and the Darwinist ultras), you dismiss it as childish gibberish, at odds with almost everything we know about the world. If you read it that way and take it seriously (our friends in North Kentucky), the result is even worse: you are forced to believe things about the world which are patently untrue; your whole system of evaluation collapses; it is impossible to have any discourse about anything with anyone who does not share your own view of the universe; truth is catastrophically redefined as something that fits with your reading of a few hundred words; the only place you can live is the self-erected ghetto; no one from outside can be allowed in – their ideas are infectious and cause spiritual death.

Genesis, however, is not a simple book. Its apparent simplicity is a result of exhaustive refining. As any author knows, it takes a particularly long time to write a particularly short book. Every syllable of the Hebrew has been picked up and examined minutely by the original scholarly compilers. They looked through many lenses. They looked at the numeric connotations of the letters that were used; they looked at the parallelism between paragraphs; they looked at how the whole scheme would be read by Jews encountering Mesopotamian myths. They structured the chapters deliberately, elaborately and resonantly, piling up their bricks in forms that were themselves intended to expound the whole. They laid allusion upon allusion, cementing the whole thing with *gematria*.[2] It coruscates with nuance. The compilers had the same weapons in their literary armoury as we do. They deployed metaphor, simile, analogy, parable, irony, paradox, parabola, understatement, humour and echoing, eloquent silence. They knew a poem when they heard one, and a contradiction when they saw one. If they read the assertions on the Answers in Genesis website, they would not at first know whether to laugh or to cry. But soon they would be very, very angry.

They would be angry, first of all, that the creationists could not see that Genesis 1 and Genesis 2 are wholly distinct but complementary accounts.[3] There are some barn-door discrepancies between them which indicate, if nothing else does, that the accounts are not intended to be taken literally. Genesis 1 has a cosmic perspective. It tells the classic story of the six-day creation. Vegetation appears on the third day,[4] water creatures and birds on the fifth day,[5] and land animals, followed by man, on the sixth day.[6] Genesis 2 is a much more local, anthropocentric account. Man is the first thing to appear on the scene, before even the plants appear, let alone the animals:

> In the day that the LORD God made the earth and the heavens, when no plant of the field was yet in the earth and no herb of the field had yet sprung up – for the LORD God had not caused it to rain upon the earth, and there was no one to till the ground; but a stream would rise from the earth, and water the whole face of the ground – then the LORD God formed man from the dust of the ground . . .[7]

Animals come later, as companions to man.

> Then the LORD God said, 'It is not good that the man should be alone; I will make him a helper as his partner.' So out of the ground the LORD God formed every animal of the field and every bird of the air, and brought them to the man to see what he would call them.[8]

The companionship of the animals proves inadequate for some unspecified reason, and so woman is created from the man's rib.[9]

The compilers would be angry, too, about the sheer presumption of biblical literalism. The literalists presume that simple human language, shorn of all context, poetry and mythological allusion, can tell the story of the creation of the universe. The compilers were not so arrogant. They knew that the story was far too big for that, and so they never embarked on the exercise, and made it perfectly clear (by the unmistakable contradictions and in many other ways) that this was not what they were doing.

Many things in the Genesis accounts bear an emphatic label saying 'figurative'. The idea of the 'tree of life' is lifted from the Mesopotamian myth 'The Epic of Gilgamesh'. The hero, Gilgamesh, desperate for immortality, searches long and hard for the tree, finds it and is robbed of it by a serpent. The talking snake in Genesis is plainly supposed to be an ordinary, created animal rather than some sort of spiritual force. It is a snake, it is not Satan. 'Now the serpent was more crafty than any *other* wild animal that the LORD God had made,' we are told.[10] And lest there be any doubt, God curses it in terms that make it clear: 'cursed are you among all animals and among all wild creatures'.[11] Although it is a natural, creaturely, wild snake, it talks, which might suggest that we are in the realm of the figurative. But if that is not enough, it appears that before it was cursed, it walked upright. Otherwise why would God say, in the course of his sentencing remarks, 'Because you have done this . . . upon your belly you shall go'?[12] That is another indication of its naturalness, of course. Spiritual forces do not crawl on their bellies.

Figurative use is obvious in the way Adam is described. The formulation used to denote Adam throughout the first three chapters of Genesis is *Ha Adam*. But that, in Hebrew, is not a personal name at all. It simply means 'the human'. 'Adam' is not used as a given name, to denote a particular individual, until chapter 4. Throughout the stories of the creation and the 'fall', Adam is expressly and deliberately a generic human.

There are more clues if we look properly. In chapter 4, Cain, the first-mentioned son of Adam and Eve, kills his brother Abel and God finds out, condemning him to be a fugitive. Cain is devastated at the sentence: 'I shall be a fugitive and a wanderer on the earth, and anyone who meets me may kill me.'[13] God clearly acknowledges that there is a threat from others, and makes Cain safe by putting on his forehead the famous mark.[14] Cain goes off, settles in the land of Nod, and meets his wife.[15]

But what are Cain and God worried about? According to the North Kentuckians, they cannot have been reading their Bibles. If they had, they would have known that there was no danger from others. The only other people on the earth were (absent figuration) Cain's mother and father. And where did Cain's wife come from? Was she his sister? If so, the second recorded biblical marriage was flagrantly, disgustingly incestuous. A few chapters later both Cain and his wife would be stoned to death for it.

Is this an example of sloppy editing by those meticulous compilers? Should they have been a bit more careful to avoid this embarrassing slip? North Kentucky would not like that conclusion either.

The Bible tells us loud and clear what sort of literature we are dealing with here – and most people have been able to hear it. St Paul certainly did. Writing in the epistle to the Romans, he asserts that 'sin came into the world through one man'.[16] Well, if you read Genesis 2 the way the Young Earth creationists do, Paul got it wrong. He completely and unaccountably forgets Eve. But no: Paul reads Genesis the way that the overwhelming majority of Jewish and Christian believers have, until very recently, read it. He knows why and how it was written, and treats it accordingly. That is the only respectful way to read it.

The metaphor-phobes and the mythopaths are missing such a lot. It's a shame. It is tragic poverty. But they are also asserting a lot. Take this flippant example, from Genesis 3: '[Adam and Eve] heard the sound of the LORD God walking in the garden at the time of the evening breeze.' Was God really out strolling? If so, that presumably means that he has legs, buttocks and the sort of nervous system needed for the walking process. Indeed, the same process of literal interpretation, applied elsewhere in the Bible, allows us to conclude quite a lot about God's anatomy. He is plainly right-handed, for instance, and has a particularly strong right arm which he uses for creation, attack and defence: 'Your right hand, O LORD, glorious in power – your right hand, O LORD, shattered the enemy,'[17] is one example. There are many others.[18]

Does the sun really have a tent in the heavens? The Bible says so: 'In the heavens he has set a tent for the sun, which comes out like a bridegroom from his wedding canopy.'[19] No such tent has ever been discovered by our sophisticated telescopes. Does that mean that the Bible is unreliable?

All this is, of course, tedious nonsense – the stuff of schoolboy jokes. But, sadly, it has to be spelled out.

If you are going to be a literalist, you have to be a consistent one. If you are going to make it an article of faith that each of the six days of creation was twenty-four hours long, and that the Genesis chronologies make the earth six thousand years old, you have a lot of work to do. You must contend to the death that the scientists are wrong in asserting that the sky is not a dome with waters swirling above it.[20] Whenever a scientist says that the moon is not a lamp but a mirror, you must contradict him in the name of the truth.[21] You have to deny the Big Bang, because the earth seems to have existed in some form before light did.[22] You have to invoke an explanation for the illumination of the earth on day one and the mornings and evenings of days one, two and three. The sun will not do: that did not exist until day four.[23, 24] You have to fight against the monstrous error that the earth spins on its axis, or moves round the sun.[25] And so on. You would be better off closing your ears to such scurrilous heresy, which is of course what creationists generally do.

Creationism has systematically unlearned not only most of the scientific advances of the last three thousand years, but also much of the theological understanding. Calvin, a man not noted for his flabby liberalism, observed in his commentary on Genesis: 'Nothing is here treated of but the visible form of the world. He who would learn astronomy, and other recondite arts, let him go elsewhere.'[26]

Quite. The Bible is not a science textbook. If it were, and if it gave an adequately explicit account of the technicalities of creation, I certainly could not understand it, nor could its compilers and nor, I dare say, could either Richard Dawkins or the denizens of North Kentucky.

The Bible *has* to condescend to be useful. An important part of its condescension is that it uses human language – the language of a people embedded in their time and their culture. Yes, it is literarily sophisticated, but that sophistication does not begin to match the size of its subject. Yes, it is complex, but not by the standards of the double helix. Genesis is not written in the mathematical equations which would no doubt be necessary to describe *what* was happening during the process by which things came to be. Nor does it inscribe in esoteric, Kabbalistic symbols, accessible only to a hermetic priesthood, an account of *why* things happened. Yes, there is mystery. The language often strains to near or beyond breaking point to express it. That creates real difficulties. But the whole point of the Bible is accessibility: it is about God speaking, and speaking not only to create, but also to be heard. It is desperate to be heard about the really important things: who we are, why we are here, where we have come from, where we are going, and how to live. As he went into the actual gutter in first-century Palestine (according to the Christians), so God, in the first chapters of the first book, goes down into the linguistic gutter in an effort to be understood and available. Calvin again: 'Moses does not speak with philosophical acuteness on occult mysteries, but relates those things which are everywhere observed, even by the uncultivated, and which are in common use.'[27] And those things did not, and do not, include partial differential equations, the biochemistry of the mitochondria or the optics of the cephalopod eye.

There is almost universal scholarly agreement that the Genesis accounts are at least in part polemical documents, designed to contradict the view of the world and the gods enshrined in the competing Mesopotamian and Egyptian religions. It is an anti-polytheistic tract. 'In the beginning, God . . .' it starts.[28] Not gods, and not creatures. The book opens by the clearest possible assertion that there is God (and only one of them), and there are creatures. They are not the same. There is a colossal divide. To worship anything created is to make a basic and terribly dangerous mistake.

The lesson is repeated again and again.[29] The astrological cults of Mesopotamia and Egypt are subtly but unmistakably insulted. In Genesis, the sun, moon and stars are all created together on day four, after the plants.[30] Since light was created on day one,[31] this is of course scientific nonsense – and the compilers knew it. They knew where light came from. But it makes admirable polemical sense. The heavens are being demoted. Not only are they expressly *created* things, but they also follow meekly after the plants in the created order. 'It would make more sense to worship a cabbage than to bow down to the stars,' the Bible is saying. And there is still more denigration. The sun and the moon are rather like household lamps, calendars and watches. They are everyday things: you use them to light the room and to remind you of dates and times.[32] They do not use or rule you. Only a fool prostrates himself before the kitchen clock.

In the catalogue of the created order everything, once it is created, is said to be 'good': everything, that is, apart from man[33] and the sky.[34] The message is clear enough: do not look either to yourselves or to the sky for your guidance.

The week is reclaimed from its bondage to the sky. The Mesopotamians had seven-day lunar cycles, and in obeisance to the moon, the seventh day was a fast day – a day of ill luck. You had it wrong, says the Bible: the seventh day has nothing to do with the moon. And to make the break explicit, the seventh day becomes not a time to fast, fear and mourn, but a time to celebrate.[35]

In case the reader misses it, the point is rammed home still harder in the summary of the first week's work. 'These are the generations of the heavens and the earth when they were created,' it says.[36] It is an odd, rather clumsy formulation for anyone not familiar with Mesopotamian religion. But the contemporary readers would have picked up the reference immediately. It is a biting satire on the elaborate genealogies of the gods and goddesses of Mesopotamian cosmogony. 'This is the *real* family tree of your supposedly divine star and moon deities,' the author is saying. 'And you can see that they were all shaped, and quite late in the day too, by the one true God – the one we worship.'

Later on in Genesis, and elsewhere in the Bible, the allusions to the Mesopotamian myths become even more explicit. Any pious Mesopotamian would be shocked and appalled at the blasphemy of Psalm 104, which talks about the great sea monster, Leviathan, being formed by God 'to sport' in the sea.[37] In Mesopotamian mythology, sea monsters were among the elemental forces of chaos which had to be defeated by the creator before the business of creation could begin. But to these flippant Hebrews and their God, these awesome monsters (mere creatures, like everything else) have *entertainment* value: they frolic around like goldfish in a bowl. This God must have seemed supremely confident, with an irreverent side wholly unfamiliar, terribly disconcerting and rather unbecoming in a god. He seems to like having fun – very unlike the dark, thirsty gods of Mesopotamia who sternly supped sacrificial blood from a stone. Indeed, this God was not interested in burnt meat or pleased by the screams of costly cows. He did not see humans as slaves, either, but in a sense demanded more; he delegated a good deal of the management of the world to them – and (since men were all made in his image) to all of them, not just the kings.[38]

So much for the background: what does the Genesis account have to contribute to our knowledge of the natural world? (We return later, and in a lot more detail, to the story of man and the garden of Eden. Man might turn out to be a very special case indeed.) We have seen not only that the book is neither history nor science, but that it goes out of its way to remind us that it is not. Should it then be mentioned at all in any attempt to make sense of biology? Well, yes: it does purport to deal in broad terms with origins and with the nature of the relationship between the author and his creatures. Those origins and that relationship have some specifically zoological and botanical corollaries. It lets us feel the intended texture of life's fabric. Certainly if we ever think, looking at anything on the earth, 'That's wonderful,' or, 'Surely that's not how it's meant to be,' Genesis has a great deal to say.

Genesis deals with origins, yes; but does it deal with absolute beginnings – creation *ex nihilo*? It is not clear that it does. The first two words of the Bible are deeply odd and almost always mistranslated. They actually say, '*In beginning*, God created the heavens and the earth.'[39] They are generally rendered, 'In *the* beginning . . .' The definite article cannot be inferred. It imports a whole set of presumptions that the Bible itself does not make. Without the article, the first sentence writhes with fascinating possibilities. In beginning *what*? Everything that there is? This particular local segment of a much bigger story? The subsequent bits of the sentence do nothing to dispel the mystery. The Hebrew word translated 'created' (*bara*) does not necessarily mean making something out of nothing.[40] It can mean re-creation.[41] And indeed, the plain reading of the first couple of verses suggests strongly that at the beginning of the story Genesis is telling, there was already something in existence. The earth was an amorphous thing, plunged in darkness, with waters swirling over it; but it did exist. 'In the beginning when God created the heavens and the earth, the earth was a formless void and darkness covered the face of the deep, while a wind from God swept over the face of the waters.'[42] The subsequent act of 'creation' is not the spontaneous generation of matter from nothing – not the production of cosmological rabbits from a divine hat – but a process of remodelling, dividing, ordering and calling things forth from what already exists. The waters above are separated from the waters below;[43] the waters under the sky are gathered into one place;[44] the earth 'puts forth' vegetation;[45] the waters 'bring forth' swarms of living creatures;[46] and the earth 'brings forth' living creatures of all kinds.[47] Of the things on the earth, only man seems to have come specifically and individually from the lathe of God; he alone is not 'brought forth' from the already created world: 'So God created humankind in his image.'[48] Yet even man, in the second creation story, was made 'from the dust of the ground'[49] – precisely the same stuff from which the animals are later made.[50]

All this sounds eerily familiar. It is a reasonable description of the process of evolution – the emergence of X from Y. When the earth 'brings forth' something, the sense is 'Let something within come out.'[51] In the second creation story, the Hebrew talks about 'every shrub of the field before it was in the earth',[52] almost as if there was already some sort of Platonic type to which the actual plants would later approximate. The plants and the animals are in some sense *inherent* in the earth. The order in which things appear in the first creation account broadly parallels the order that modern science would give.[53] Genesis even talks about a common ancestor – the dust. Re-label the biblical dust 'DNA', and you have a fair approximation to the neo-Darwinian synthesis.

Both North Oxford and North Kentucky would howl loudly in protest at this. If forced to articulate the howl into argument, the argument of each of them would coalesce around the Genesis account of 'species'. They would both assert that Genesis teaches the fixity of species. Such teaching is, of course, anathema to Darwinians.

We see in a moment that Genesis does not suggest, let alone insist on, the immutability of species. But before we come to that, would it really be so catastrophic to the credibility of Genesis if it did suggest it? Hardly. It is not only that we are not dealing with a scientific textbook. Species themselves, mutable or not, still remain an important analytical category – so important that Darwin wrote a book to try to explain their origins, modern evolutionists struggle manfully to prove that enough micro-evolution can eventually produce them, and modern taxonomists pay their gas bills on the basis of a universal and perfectly sensible assumption that 'species' means something.

What does Genesis actually say? The obvious references are as follows.

• *Plants*: 'Then God said, "Let the earth put forth vegetation: plants yielding seed, and fruit trees of every kind on earth that bear fruit with the seed in it." And it was so. The earth brought forth vegetation: plants yielding seed of every kind, and trees of every kind bearing fruit with the seed in it.'[54]

- *Birds and water-dwelling animals*: 'And God said, "Let the waters bring forth swarms of living creatures, and let birds fly above the earth across the dome of the sky." So God created the great sea monsters and every living creature that moves, of every kind, with which the waters swarm, and every winged bird of every kind.'[55]
- *Terrestrial animals*: 'And God said, "Let the earth bring forth living creatures of every kind: cattle and creeping things and wild animals of the earth of every kind." And it was so. God made the wild animals of the earth of every kind, and the cattle of every kind, and everything that creeps upon the ground of every kind.'[56]

'Kind' is probably better translated 'type'. The Hebrew word is used fairly often in biblical lists of animals.[57] It does not imply 'species' in the technical sense in which it is used by biologists, and the sense in which it is used in the creation accounts does not begin to imply any sort of genetic fixity. It simply indicates that the types of animals and plants (or some of them) that the compilers would have seen wandering round in their world were 'brought forth' because God thought that they should be. It says nothing about how those types should or should not be expected to transmute subsequently.

Perhaps some of the creationist obsession with the alleged immutability of species is a result of the translation that a large proportion of them reads – the King James Version. Many conservative Christians think and say that this is the only valid version; that there was a special sort of divine inspiration of its translators; that the history of subsequent Bible translation – rather like the history of post-Noahic evolution – has been a history of degeneracy, with truths being shed like genetic information.

The King James Version talks about the plants and animals

being created 'after their kind'. There is a clear and entirely artificial implication here that there is some sort of prototypic animal or plant – 'a kind', almost a Platonic form. But that is not what the text says.

Apart from the plain reading of the key texts, there are other, more subtle suggestions that Genesis does not teach the immutability of species. There are, for instance, some significant omissions from the catalogues of organisms in Genesis. There are no amphibians. Genesis talks about the creation of water creatures[58] and land creatures,[59] but not things that bridge the gap.[60]

If you are a creationist, that is rather embarrassing. You can hardly say that the editors forgot about amphibians. The Israelites were a particularly frog-aware nation.[61] You have to say that all amphibians are a result of post-creation pseudo-speciation – the same genetic degeneration that led to dingoes being produced from the prototypic dog-on-the-ark. A similar point can be made about the vegetation (Genesis does not mention all the categories). And what about the whole prokaryotic world?

And now into deeper waters – waters in which may possibly be found further suggestions that natural selection was built into the whole system from the beginning, or was at least acknowledged and for some reason tolerated.

The text makes two announcements in relation to each creative act.[62] First God announces that something will happen: 'Let there be light', 'Let the earth put forth vegetation', 'Let there be lights in the dome of the sky', and so on. And then there is an announcement that the act has been accomplished: 'And there was light', 'And it was so'. But there is a strange discordance between the two sets of announcements – a discordance audible only in the Hebrew. Only in the case of the light is there a perfect match: only the light does *precisely* what it is told to do. 'Let light be,' commands God; 'Light be,' comes back the report.[63] This is not ham-fisted editing: whoever put this story together knew exactly what they were doing. 'Grass grass,' God tells the earth. But the earth does not. It 'puts forth' grass.[64] The created order is slightly disobedient from the start. Initially the disobedience is apparently slight: it can be expressed by a tiny grammatical nuance. But as the story goes on, the disobedience crescendoes. When God asks the waters to 'bring forth' the water animals,[65] we do not hear that this is what happened at all. There is not even any 'And it was so'. To get what he has ordained, God is forced, for the very first time, to create directly: 'So God created the great sea monsters and every living creature that moves, of every kind, with which the waters swarm.'[66] He gets the result that he wanted, but not, apparently, by quite the mechanism that he intended.

Perhaps the resistance to order described in the text can be traced back even earlier.[67] God orders that light and darkness should separate completely.[68] But they do not obey. In the very next verse we read, 'And there was evening and there was morning . . .'[69] There was dawn and there was twilight. Illegitimately, light and dark were already mingling.

A little later, in the Levitical food laws, we see further signs of uprising. George Caird notes, 'Among creatures which the Levitical code declares to be unclean . . . are all beasts and birds of prey . . . are we not dealing here with a naïve expression of the idea that nature red in tooth and claw has in some measure escaped the control of the divine holiness?'[70]

Right at the very beginning – if not before the beginning spoken of in Genesis – there are the seeds of rebellion. Or perhaps a pre-existing rebellion has not been completely quelled. Order has been brought out of the formless void, but the order is not quite complete.

If this is so, why does God describe everything (bar the sky and man) as 'good', and why, standing back on the sixth day and surveying his handiwork, does he say that the whole created order is 'very good'?[71]

This description causes horrific difficulties. If the world that was being admired by God was the natural world we now see, it presumably means that God thinks predation, waste, selfishness and death are 'good'. If that is what he thinks, and 'good' has any ethical or aesthetic connotations, I am afraid that I cannot agree with him. (I argue the case for my non-agreement in the next chapter.) If one could design a world that would not have any pain, but would still achieve what it is meant to achieve, it is surely not morally good to opt for the painful solution. If you could have the beauty of a lion's spring without the scream, the dislocation and the haemorrhage that follows it, would that not be better than what you do see in the Serengeti? And as for aesthetics, this surely follows from the morality. If something is evil, it is not aesthetically good. Porn is not art.

There are several ways out of the difficulty. We look at them in more detail later. But a few preliminary points must be made here.

First, 'good' seems not to have any real moral content. Indeed, it is rather difficult to see how it could. How can one talk meaningfully about light, the sky or plants being morally good? Particularly since the Bible expressly warns its readers about drawing moral lessons from the created order instead of directly from God. Yes, the heavens may declare the glory of God,[72] but you get your directions for living from your Bible and (because you are made in the image of God) your conscience.

The aesthetic possibility is rather more troubling. It is not nice to think of God revelling in the sight of avoidable animal agony. And here we have to go back to the text. In his great commentary on Genesis, Westermann observes that 'good' is more a comment on creation's functionality and its fitness for purpose than on its beauty of creation.[73] If that is right, God might simply be saying, 'That works,' and, 'The whole lot works really well.' This exculpates God from the charge of obscene voyeurism. But it does not help him if the really serious charge is (and it is) that he could have made the world differently but failed to do so.

Second, the world that God was observing might not have been the world that we see. Perhaps it really was wonderful, pain-free and placid at the time he was describing it. Perhaps he should not be blamed for making the world that we complain of, because he made a very different one which went unavoidably wrong. Perhaps the whole created order was transformed radically by the 'fall'.

The trouble with all this is that we know that there never was a time when natural selection's competition did not operate. If there was a historical 'fall' of man which is linked in some way to the disgusting animal suffering that we see, it was undoubtedly preceded by many millions of years of animal suffering, predation and death. We have already reviewed the evidence for this. Dinosaurs had meat-ripping teeth and tumours long before any man was around to fall.

Is this a complete impasse? Are there any other connotations? There is just one more. It demands a fundamental re-evaluation of the nature of the Genesis story, and it depends on the food that the creatures were supposed to eat.

To man God said, 'See, I have given you every plant yielding seed that is upon the face of all the earth, and every tree with seed in its fruit; you shall have them for food.'[74]

To the animals and the birds God gave 'every green plant for food'.[75] The text declares, 'And it was so.'[76]

But it very clearly was *not* so. If you maintain that Genesis insists on actual, historical vegetarian lions, you consign the whole book to a cabinet of grotesque mythological curiosities. It was not so according to the fossil record, but, much more importantly for present purposes, it was not so to the certain knowledge of the Genesis compilers. They had looked into a dog's mouth; they had heard the desert lions roaring. They knew that there had never been *actual* vegetarian lions, and they knew, too, the sort of literature they were writing. This part of the story tells us not about what happened, but about God's dream for the world. Not only is it not science; it is neither history nor purported history. It is a statement of original intention and eventual outcome. It is a mission statement. It is prophecy. The first chapter of the Bible is just as much an apocalyptic vision as the last chapter.[77]

The prophecy was picked up very explicitly by Isaiah. There, too, we see vegetarian carnivores:

> The wolf shall live with the lamb,
>   the leopard shall lie down with the kid,
> the calf and the lion and the fatling together . . .
> The cow and the bear shall graze,
>   their young shall lie down together;
>   and the lion shall eat straw like the ox.
> The nursing child shall play over the hole of the asp,
>   and the weaned child shall put its hand on the adder's den.
> They will not hurt or destroy
>   on all my holy mountain:
> for the earth will be full of the knowledge of the LORD
>   as the waters cover the sea.[78]

The Genesis story of universal vegetarianism tells us not that wolves ever ate cucumbers, but that God's reaction to animal pain is the same as ours is or should be: he is disgusted. He created a world that worked – that was 'very good' in that sense. The verdict 'very good' is pronounced on the placid, vegetarian world. He would never have said that about the Ngorongoro Crater. Nor, from what we can see in Genesis, would he ever have endorsed – let alone have designed – an engine for a continued, evolving creation which was necessarily fuelled by pain, selfishness and waste.

Unfortunately there is still another twist that must be unravelled. Because, of course, men and animals in the Bible did not remain vegetarian. Later in the Genesis story God expressly allows men to be carnivorous. It is a very weird story indeed.

God, appalled at human behaviour, decides to eliminate all life on earth apart from Noah, Noah's family and the animals that will travel in the ark with Noah. The only food permitted on the ark is the vegetable food specified in the creation stories.[79] The flood comes, followed by the sun, which dries up the water. When Noah emerges from the ark the very first thing that he does, in apparently blatant disregard of the vegetarian edict in Genesis 1, and wholly unprompted by God, is to murder sacrificially some of the animals and birds that had been his companions over the past months – animals, remember, that were the only ones left of their type. Perhaps there had been some breeding on the ark, producing some spares, but not all of the 'clean' animals have such fast breeding cycles that there would have been spares of them all.

'Then Noah built an altar to the LORD, and took of every clean animal and of every clean bird, and offered burnt-offerings on the altar.'[80] God's response is curious: 'when the LORD smelt the pleasing odour, the LORD said in his heart, "I will never again curse the ground because of humankind, for the inclination of the human heart is evil from youth . . .' And it is not only humans who have disobeyed the original vegetarian injunction: it seems that the animals themselves have acquired an illegitimate taste for one another's flesh: 'Now the earth was corrupt in God's sight, and the earth was filled with violence. And God saw that the earth was corrupt; for all flesh had corrupted its ways upon the earth.'[81] God then changes dramatically the Genesis relationship between man and the animals and between animals themselves:

> God blessed Noah and his sons, and said to them, 'Be fruitful and multiply, and fill the earth. The fear and dread of you shall rest on every animal of the earth, and on every bird of the air, on everything that creeps on the ground, and on all the fish of the sea; into your hand they are delivered. Every moving thing that lives shall be food for you; and just as I gave you the green plants, I give you everything. Only, you shall not eat flesh with its life, that is, its blood.'[82]

Is God not being hugely inconsistent? Only eight short chapters earlier he was saying (if we have read him right) that he loathed the idea of his creatures grazing on each other rather than on the grass; that he hated the sound of animal screams in the night; that he wanted his creation to be characterised by placid co-existence, not predatory enmity; that man was supposed to be a caretaker, not a butcher. Has he changed his mind?

No, he has not. What we have here is a resigned dispensation, not a statement of God's chosen plan for the world. God is throwing up his hands and saying, 'Man, to whom I gave free will, is clearly going to exercise that free will in the direction of violence against the creation.' That is the context of the comment about evil inclination. God despairs of man, in man's own strength, becoming the sort of creature he was meant to be. Entirely predictably, human free will has failed: more radical solutions will eventually be needed. But in the meantime, as a damage limitation exercise, man's violent tendencies can be placed inside a restraining framework – the laws which are then given. The laws remind man very explicitly of the reasons why they were given: no thoughtful human going to all the trouble and expense of excluding blood from his meat should ever forget that the reason for all the nuisance was God's original intention that no blood should be spilled at all.

Possibly, too, the dispensation is linked crucially to the command: 'Be fruitful and multiply, and fill the earth.'[83] As we will see, killing and eating animals, if you can do it efficiently, is a very good nutritional strategy: one zebra is worth a thousand cabbages. Or perhaps it is a response to the possibility that the animals might obey with dangerous enthusiasm their own injunction in Genesis 1 to 'be fruitful and multiply'. If there is any truth in either of these suggestions, the dispensation is long, long redundant. We are killing animals and wiping out species faster than in any of the great geological extinctions.

This is all very well, but we should not lose sight of the central problem. Despite God's apparent distaste for them, selfishness, pain and waste *were* apparently the fuel for an engine that seems to have produced much of the diversity in the world. Who built *that* engine? Some of the footprints of the culprit have already been noted in those quirky little signs of primordial disobedience. Before we ever get to the garden of Eden, something was beginning to go wrong.

Indeed, we do not have to be subtle to see this. Evil was not injected into a morally pristine world by anything that Adam or Eve did or did not do. There was a snake already in the garden, whispering wicked things.

It seems that God expected trouble from whatever it was that had been incompletely subdued at the time of creation. Why else commission man to 'subdue' the earth?[84] You subdue things that rise up against you. In chapter 8 we embark on a detailed search for the culprit.

First, however, we need to decide if we are making too much fuss about the pain and suffering inherent in the natural world. I have asserted that it is bad, and therefore amounts to a problem;

I have not argued it. We have looked at the meaning of 'good' and 'very good' as they are used in the Genesis account, and seen that they mean something like 'fit for purpose'. But that is of limited help in exculpating an apparently omnipotent God from the charge of designing a universe with selfishness and pain at its core, when it might have been otherwise. God apparently dislikes the selfishness and pain very much indeed. That plea opens the way to a possible defence that he is not omnipotent after all. But before going down that road, we ought to explore whether we and God are being too squeamish. Perhaps there is nothing wrong with all that animal suffering after all.

To ensure that we are not giving God an unfair advantage, we will forget, for the purposes of the next chapter, the optimism that came when we looked at the issue of altruism. We go into the woods again, but this time the clouds are very dark.

CHAPTER 7

The Ethical Problem: '. . . and it was very good'

God saw everything that he had made, and indeed, it was very
good.

(Genesis 1:31)

Look round this universe. What an immense profusion of beings,
animated and organized, sensible and active! You admire this
prodigious variety and fecundity. But inspect a little more
narrowly these living existences, the only beings worth regarding.
How hostile and destructive to each other! How insufficient all
of them for their own happiness! How contemptible or odious
to the spectator! The whole presents nothing but the idea of a
blind nature, impregnated by a great vivifying principle, and
pouring forth from her lap, without discernment or parental
care, her maimed and abortive children.

(David Hume, *Dialogues Concerning Natural Religion*)[1]

A well-meaning friend gave my children a DVD. It was called
My Father's World, and consisted of happy scenes to the musical
backdrop of Christian worship songs. A school of dolphins
leaped playfully through a sea of cliché blue, unmangled by
orcas. A relaxed squirrel nibbled nuts, with no pine marten
crouched to spring. Brightly coloured fish swam in co-operative ballet over a coral reef, with not a shark in sight. An anteater
waddled through an apparently jaguar-free stretch of South
America. Nothing writhed in the poisonous tentacles of the
dazzlingly lovely jellyfish. A lion looked contentedly over the

veldt, only aesthetically interested in the herd of zebra. There was an unnaturally high incidence of rainbows. A Canada goose dabbled for food in the shallows, juxtaposed with a child in a swimming pool: they were both evidently on vacation. 'How great is our God,' went the song in the background, as a cartoon hippo descended on a parachute, with no obvious leeches hanging out of its mouth. 'You give and take away,' another song poignantly reminded us, but to footage of children playing and a top spinning, rather than of a children's hospice or a tiger kill.

This is the view of much of the Christian world. If that is your view, there is no problem at all. You will see no difficulty, and much encouragement, in having posters on your walls showing natural habitats with quotations from the Psalms stamped on them. When you go for a walk in the woods you will not see it as a trip to the abattoir. No questions will leap to your lips when you are told that God is good. You will sing rumbustiously and without embarrassment:

When through the woods and forest glades I wander
>   And hear the birds sing sweetly in the trees;
>   When I look down from lofty mountain grandeur
>   And hear the brook and feel the gentle breeze:
> Then sings my soul, my Saviour God, to Thee:
>   How great Thou art, how great Thou art![2]

Another Christian song concludes, 'Whoever made such a wonderful world, is someone I can believe in.'[3]

I too can believe in him, but despite, not because of, the fact that I look out at the world. The undoubted wonder there is a terrible wonder. The view in the DVD cannot survive a five-minute look down a decent microscope or a ten-minute read of any ecology textbook.

Everyone who has looked hard and honestly at the world has

been terrified and troubled by what they have seen there. The faith of many has been wrecked on the rocks of animal suffering.

In 1856, Darwin wrote to Hooker, 'What a book a Devil's Chaplain might write on the clumsy, wasteful, blundering, low and horridly cruel works of nature.'[4] In 1860, he spelled out the consequences for his own theology of his observations of the biological world: 'I cannot persuade myself that a benefi- cent and omnipotent God would have designedly created the *Ichneumonidae* with the express intention of their feeding within the living bodies of caterpillars.'

Before we mention the particular problems posed by the Darwinian view of the world, it is as well to note that (subject to the comments we will come to later about just how sensate organisms are, and how intelligent it is to talk about animal suffering) animal suffering is ubiquitous. Take any route you like from the North Pole to the South Pole, and you will find at every point fairly sophisticated neurones, not all that different from our own, shouting things to their control centres which, if translated into human language, would be: 'Pain, pain, pain.' The neuronal yells per square foot rise to a frantic peak in the tropics. The more lush and bountiful the landscape, the more crushing the weight of the suffering. The sheer amount of suffering (as opposed to the mere occurrence of suffering) is philosophically important. 'Much of the problem of evil, both moral and physical, lies in its scale,' writes John Polkinghorne.[5] It makes it harder to say flippantly about the fall, 'Well, yes, that bent things a bit.' We are not talking here about minor grazes on the knees of creation: we are talking about massive, universal, crippling deformity.

I once went to a talk on the problem of evil. It was an entirely splendid talk, apart from one unfortunate, over-homely metaphor. The speaker, trying to convince us that we all recog- nised the problem of evil in some form or other (surely an unnecessary exercise), painted a picture of a happy picnic in a sunlit field. 'But there's always a wasp buzzing round somewhere, isn't there?' she said. That misrepresents the *nature* of the problem: there is more sting than lemonade. The wasp is more of the essence of the picnic than are the ham sandwiches.

That brings us to the particular problems inherent in the indisputable fact that natural selection has generated much of the colour, the complexity and the beauty that are so uncritically admired on Christian DVDs and wall posters. Let's assume that God has chosen or permitted natural selection to do that generating. How does that leave him looking?

The American biologist George Williams stated well the primary case against God: it is a biologically sophisticated restatement of the age-old problem of pain:

> With what other than condemnation is a person with any moral sense supposed to respond to a system in which the ultimate purpose in life is to be better than your neighbor at getting genes into future generations, in which those successful genes provide the message that instructs the development of the next generation, in which that message is always 'exploit your environment, including your friends and relatives, so as to maximise our genes' success', in which the closest thing to a golden rule is 'don't cheat, unless it is likely to provide a net benefit'?[6]

We find similar comments whenever we browse through the reflections of thoughtful biologists. Here is David Hull:

> What kind of God can one infer from the sort of phenomena epitomized by the species on Darwin's Galapagos Islands? The evolutionary process is rife with happenstance, contingency, incredible waste, death, pain and horror . . . Whatever the God implied by evolutionary theory and the data of natural selection may be like, he is not the Protestant God of waste not,

want not. He is also not the loving God who cares about his productions. He is not even the awful God pictured in the Book of Job. The God of the Galapagos is careless, wasteful, indifferent, almost diabolical. He is certainly not the sort of God to whom anyone would be inclined to pray.[7]

If one gathers the evidence for God solely from the biological world, there are three possible consequences: atheism, a belief that God is powerless to do things differently, or a belief that God is malevolent. Assuming that God could do things differently, the malevolence of God is a real possibility. 'The problem is not of ceasing to believe in God,' wrote C.S. Lewis in the aftermath of his wife's death, 'but of coming to believe such terrible things about him.'[8] Is he a cosmic vet or a cosmic vivisector? 'At all times,' wrote Lewis elsewhere, 'an inference from the course of events in this world to the goodness and wisdom of the Creator would have been equally preposterous, and it was never made.'[9]

Pascal makes the same point:

> I wonder at the hardihood with which such persons undertake to talk about God. In a treatise to infidels they begin with a chapter proving the existence of God from the works of Nature . . . This only gives their readers grounds for thinking that the proofs of our religion are very weak . . . It is a remarkable fact that no canonical writer has ever used Nature to prove God.[10]

Or, he might have added, to prove the benevolence or omnipotence of God. And why not? Because it cannot coherently be done. And it cannot coherently be done because there is a real, solid problem there which cannot easily be transmuted into an apologetic benefit.

The Bible, on the face of it, seems to make the problem worse, not better. While it implies, as we have seen in the story of the vegetarian lions, that God did not want things the way they are (which might begin to look like a plea of guilty to the allegation of non-omnipotence), elsewhere God seems to be comfortable with the idea of both human and animal suffering. Psalm 104, for instance, tells us, 'The young lions roar for their prey, seeking their food from God.'[11] That sounds rather like divine acquiescence with the occupying forces of predation – the very forces that we have been seeking to say are fighting against God's intended order. In Job, God expressly acknowledges, without obvious breast-beating, the waste inherent in the natural order: 'For [the ostrich] it leaves its eggs to the earth, and lets them be warmed on the ground,' he rather dispassionately notes, 'forgetting that a foot may crush them, or that a wild animal may trample them.'[12]

The Old Testament seethes with God's bloodthirsty acts and threats against his opponents. Joshua is told to institute a policy of ethnic cleansing against the Canaanites, sparing neither woman nor child. In Isaiah, the very book that contains the Edenic vision of the restored creation in which the wolf lies down with the lamb, God repeatedly and violently fulminates against the heathen. Here is one example, a highly explicit and thoroughly international excoriation, all with musical background:

> The LORD will cause his majestic voice to be heard and the descending blow of his arm to be seen, in furious anger and a flame of devouring fire, with a cloudburst and tempest and hailstones. The Assyrian will be terror-stricken at the voice of the LORD, when he strikes with his rod. And every stroke of the staff of punishment that the LORD lays upon him will be to the sound of timbrels and lyres; battling with brandished arm he will fight with him. For his burning-place has long been prepared; truly it is made ready for the king, its pyre made deep and wide, with fire and wood in abundance; the breath of the LORD, like a stream of sulphur, kindles it.[13]

Deep down God might be a vegetarian, but he talks like a carnivore. It is wise to remember that we are not dealing with a tame lion.

Bringing humans, let alone nations, into the picture can obscure things. Humans, with their possibly unique capacity for free will and hence rebellion, are certainly very special animals. Not all explanations for their suffering translate in even a garbled form to the rainforest or the coral reef. Let's stick for the moment to the problem of suffering in the non-human world.

While noting the facts of predation, and hearing the howls, there are still some who, hoping to get God off the charges of callousness or non-omnipotence he faces, deny that there is a problem. They say either that animals do not experience pain, or that if animals do, it has no moral significance.

The second of these arguments has a long, exalted and wholly dishonourable place in Christian philosophy. 'Reason has not been given to [animals] to have in common with us,' held Augustine, 'and so, by the most just ordinances of the Creator, both their life and their death is subject to our use.'[14] Thomas Aquinas agreed: 'It is not wrong for man to make use of [animals] either by killing them or in any other way whatever,'[15] he wrote, opening the way for the sinister Jesuit theologian Joseph Rickaby to assert that 'Brute beasts not having understanding and there-fore not being persons, cannot have any rights . . . we have no duties of charity or duties of any kind to the lower animals, as neither to sticks or stones.'[16]

Probably the mere citation of these passages will cause most modern readers to reject them. There is a deeply unattractive arrogance and callousness about them. Our conscience tells us that this must be wrong, and our conscience, here at any rate, is a useful dialectic barometer. But if our conscience does not see off Aquinas, theology and biology should.

Theology: one might seek to derive this attitude from Genesis 1, with all its talk about having dominion over the animals and subduing the earth. One might say that if man was authorised to treat animals that way, animals cannot be worth much. But that reading of Genesis 1 is wholly at odds with Genesis 2, which has the animals as companions for man (albeit not companions as adequate as woman), and man as a smock-wearing steward, not a hunt-coat-wearing king.[17, 18] We are to *care* for creation – a commission not undermined, as already demonstrated, by the odd injunction to Noah. The over-whelmingly prominent biblical attitude is that of the prophecy in Isaiah. This is demonstrated very dramatically in Jesus' atti-tudes to animals (to which we will come in detail later). He would find Rickaby even more offensive than we do.

Biology: Aquinas' attitude to animals presupposes that they have no consciousness. I argue below that even if animals are 'unconscious' in the sense that is meant here, that does not make the pain of a sentient creature justifiable. But, as a matter of fact, there is growing evidence of animal consciousness. Some of the evidence is outlined below.

Can it sensibly be contended that animals do not suffer?[19]

All the books on the subject assert a (real) distinction between sentience and consciousness. Sentience is, of course, the mere appreciation of a sensation of some sort. If you touch an earth-worm with a needle, it recoils. Consciousness is very different. C.S. Lewis describes it beautifully:

Suppose that three sensations follow one another – first A, then B, then C. When this happens to you, you have the expe-rience of passing through the process ABC. But note what this implies. It implies that there is something in you which stands sufficiently outside A to notice A passing away, and sufficiently outside B to notice B now beginning and coming to fill the place which A has vacated; and something which recognizes itself as the same through the transition from A to B and B to

C, so that it can say 'I have had the experience ABC.' Now this something is what I call Consciousness or Soul and the process I have just described is one of the proofs that the soul, though experiencing time, is not itself completely 'timeful'.[20]

This distinction is used by Lewis and others to suggest that much of the 'suffering' in the animal world that so troubles us is not suffering at all. Lewis admits that 'it is certainly difficult to suppose that the apes, the elephant and the higher domestic animals, have not, in some degree, a self or soul which connects experiences and gives rise to rudimentary individuality'. But he goes on, 'at least a great deal of what appears to be animal suffering need not be suffering in any real sense. It may be we who have invented the "sufferers" by the "pathetic fallacy" of reading into the beasts a self for which there is no real evidence.'[21]

There are two responses to this. The first is to say that Lewis is out of date: there is now real and growing evidence of animal consciousness. The second is to say that even if no animals are conscious, the distinction between sentience and consciousness does not diminish the real magnitude of the problem.

It has long been believed by most in the field that higher primates (the best studied have been chimpanzees) have some 'theory of mind' – some ability to think themselves into the position of another in a way that implies or constitutes self-consciousness. But this does not seem to be restricted to our close evolutionary cousins. Dolphins recognise themselves in mirrors, and may be smarter than chimps. Nor does consciousness seem to be a consequence of a brain with a blueprint similar to that of humans. New Caledonian crows have tool-making abilities apparently much greater than those of chimps, and seem to have a theory of mind. Yet bird brains have a plan radically different from those of mammals. Mammals and birds diverged evolutionarily at a time when the obviously cognitive bits of the brain were exceedingly rudimentary.

Simon Conway Morris believes (and makes the case for the belief with great force and credibility) that we have seriously underestimated both the incidence and the degree of cognition in the animal world, and also that cognition and consciousness have, just like the camera eye, sprung up and evolved independently several times. The universe seems readily to generate and prefer conscious creatures.[22]

Thus consciousness, even if not ubiquitous, might be common in the fields, forests and seas, and getting more common. If so, and if consciousness is what determines the moral relevance of what happens to an animal's nerve-endings, the sentience/consciousness distinction might not get rid of anything like as much problematic suffering as Lewis thought.

Let's assume, however, for the sake of argument, that man is the sole possessor of consciousness, and that when a chimpanzee is stabbed three times it merely experiences three deeply unpleasant sensations, without any 'soul' or anything akin to a 'soul' hovering over it, linking the sensations together and commenting: 'Those unpleasant sensations are happening to a thing that I call myself.' Is the stabber of such an 'unconscious' chimp any less culpable than the stabber of an ensouled chimp? Is someone who could have restrained the stabber, but failed to do so, any less culpable than in the case of an attack on a chimp with a soul? If so, why? One might argue that the culpability of an offence depends on the magnitude of the harm suffered, and that if consciousness increases suffering (or, in an absurdly academic way, defines suffering) it is worse to plunge a knife into a conscious creature. But surely, even if the 'suffering' is worse in the ensouled animal, it is still bad to cause the pain receptors in the non-ensouled animal to discharge. Even if the 'pain' is qualitatively different in an unconscious creature, it is still not nice. And it is not nice to do things that are not nice.

Part of the contribution of consciousness to 'pain' or 'suffering' is presumably anticipation. A creature capable of remarking to itself, 'I have just suffered A and then B,' is better able to experience the deeply unpleasant experience of anticipating the jangle to its nerves that will result when the stick falls and delivers sensation C. But it seems likely that, whether or not they have consciousness in the technical sense, many animals have this ability to anticipate further noxious stimuli. The much-beaten dog cringes when its cruel master comes into the room, and howls when the stick is lifted yet again.

To do nasty things to sentient creatures is then, whether or not they possess consciousness, something that reflects badly, in a moral way, on the perpetrator. If my son stamped gratuitously on a mouse, I would not say, 'That's fine, Tom. It didn't possess a soul. It was interesting to watch it burst, wasn't it? And interesting to hear how it squealed before it died.' Nor would I think that Tom's stamp was any more morally acceptable because the mouse was plainly a slow one. I would not say to him, 'Excellent. That mouse obviously had genes making it a dismal runner. You have done the mouse population a good turn by eliminating this particular bearer of those genes. Natural selection salutes you.'

If even I would not do, say or think these things, should we expect less of God? No: there is a problem all right.

We will see shortly that some think that all the suffering in the natural world is a price worth paying for the variety that it generates. If you are a straightforward, untortured evolutionary theist, that is probably what you will assert. But is it? Is all the beauty of the peacock's tail, the compound eye, the biochemistry of the liver and the condor's wing worth even any of the suffering apparently involved in its production – let alone all of it?

In *The Brothers Karamazov*, Ivan puts a proposition to his pious brother, Alyosha:

> 'Tell me yourself, I challenge your answer. Imagine that you are creating a fabric of human destiny with the object of making men happy in the end, giving them peace and rest at last, but that it was essential and inevitable to torture to death only one tiny creature – that baby beating its breast with its fist, for instance – and to found that edifice on its unavenged tears, would you consent to be the architect on those conditions? Tell me, and tell the truth.'
>
> 'No, I wouldn't consent,' said Alyosha softly.[23]

Would we consent? I hope not. And if we would not, should we expect God to do so?

Earlier, Ivan has talked about the suffering of an innocent child as the price of 'harmony' in the world.

> 'I can't accept that harmony . . . I renounce the higher harmony altogether. It's not worth the tears of that one tortured child who beat itself on the breast with its little fist and prayed in its stinking outhouse, with its unexpiated tears to 'dear, kind God'! It's not worth it, because those tears are unatoned for. They must be atoned for, or there can be no harmony. But how? How are you going to atone for them? Is it possible? By their being avenged? But what do I care for avenging them? What do I care for a hell for oppressors? What good can hell do, since those children have already been tortured? And what becomes of harmony, if there is hell? I want to forgive. I want to embrace. I don't want more suffering. And if the sufferings of children go to swell the sum of sufferings which was necessary to pay for truth, then I protest that the truth is not worth such a price. I don't want the mother to embrace the oppressor who threw her son to the dogs! She dare not forgive him! Let her forgive him for herself, if she will, let her forgive the torturer for the immeasurable suffering of her

> mother's heart. But the sufferings of her tortured child she has
> no right to forgive; she dare not forgive the torturer, even if the
> child were to forgive him! And if that is so, if they dare not
> forgive, what becomes of harmony? Is there in the whole world
> a being who would have the right to forgive and could forgive?
> I don't want harmony. From love for humanity I don't want it. I
> would rather be left with the unavenged suffering. I would rather
> remain with my unavenged suffering and unsatisfied indignation,
> even if I were wrong. Besides, too high a price is asked for harmony;
> it's beyond our means to pay so much to enter on it. And so I
> hasten to give back my entrance ticket, and if I am an honest
> man I am bound to give it back as soon as possible. And that I
> am doing. It's not God that I don't accept, Alyosha, only I most
> respectfully return him the ticket.'[24]

For 'child' we might conveniently substitute 'morally guiltless organism'. For 'harmony' we might instead say 'complexity', 'progress', 'increased organisation', or any of the other terms often used to describe the fruits of evolution.

Yes, there is a problem.

The problem is far, far worse for Christians. For anyone who does not believe in a good, powerful God, observation of the natural world's brutality and apparent capriciousness engenders distaste and perhaps a vague feeling that 'it shouldn't be like this'. The theist will wrestle with the nasty things about God's character and/or power hinted at by a look through his microscope. But the Christian has to insist not only that God is basically benevolent and powerful, but also that God is *characterised* by compassion and selflessness. God is supposed to look like Jesus, and Jesus went around healing, not maiming; actively preferring the poor and the downtrodden, not saying that it was somehow good that natural selective forces had found out their weak points; declaring that the meek, not the strong, would inherit the earth; submitting himself to the point of death, not using the power he had to escape it – and, so far as we know, cocking a snook at the whole idea that the point of life was gene propagation by remaining (unusually for a first-century Jewish man) wifeless and childless until his early and wholly avoidable murder.

Even before we get to Jesus, there are similar problems. The Old Testament, as well as often portraying God as enthusiastically homicidal, insists that despite appearances,[25] God, after creating the world, did not simply walk away, leaving it to get on with things. He is somehow involved in sustaining it. If he is indeed a watchmaker, he keeps the watch wound up.

> You make springs gush forth in the valleys;
>> they flow between the hills,
> giving drink to every wild animal;
>> the wild asses quench their thirst.
> By the streams the birds of the air have their habitation;
>> they sing among the branches.
> From your lofty abode you water the mountains;
>> the earth is satisfied with the fruit of your work.
> You cause the grass to grow for the cattle,
>> and plants for people to use . . .
> The trees of the LORD are watered abundantly,
>> the cedars of Lebanon that he planted.
> In them the birds build their nests;
>> the stork has its home in the fir trees.
> The high mountains are for the wild goats;
>> the rocks are a refuge for the coneys . . .
>> the earth is full of your creatures.
> Yonder is the sea, great and wide,
>> creeping things innumerable are there,
>> living things both small and great.
> There go the ships,
>> and Leviathan that you formed to sport in it.

These all look to you
    to give them their food in due season;
when you give to them, they gather it up;
    when you open your hand, they are filled with good things.
When you hide your face, they are dismayed;
    when you take away their breath, they die
    and return to the dust.
When you send forth your spirit, they are created;
    and you renew the face of the ground.[26]

God does not just maintain things as a dutiful retainer would. He insists that he cares. 'The LORD is good to all, and his compassion is over all that he has made.'[27]

There is no possibility of an alibi defence for God. On his own account he was there at the beginning and has not moved from the scene of the crime since. Indeed, Psalm 104 looks rather like an acknowledgement of complete responsibility for the crime – a full and frank confession.

When Jesus comes into the story, things get even more complicated. He says that God knows in detail about his creatures, cares about them, and that their times and fates are in his hands.

Look at the birds of the air; they neither sow nor reap nor gather into barns, and yet your heavenly Father feeds them. Are you not of more value than they? . . . Consider the lilies of the field, how they grow; they neither toil nor spin, yet I tell you, even Solomon in all his glory was not clothed like one of these.[28]

Are not two sparrows sold for a penny? Yet not one of them will fall to the ground unperceived by your Father. And even the hairs of your head are all counted. So do not be afraid; you are of more value than many sparrows.[29]

Yes, we are worth more than many sparrows, but sparrows are nonetheless valuable to God. They are worth so much to God that he keeps an individual eye on each of them. It is getting worse for God. Jesus seems to be saying that the smoking evolutionary gun is in God's hand.

Jesus himself, say the Christians, is the ultimate apocalyptic solution of the problem of animal suffering. He came to usher in the messianic kingdom of which Isaiah spoke – the kingdom where the wolf will lie down with the lamb. When Jesus went out into the wilderness, we are told that he 'was *with* the wild beasts'[30] – a curiously strong verb, implying serious intimacy. The old enmity that followed Noah's barbecue of the animals on the ark was on its way out. What happened in the Judean desert was the first fruit of Isaiah 11, the first indication that the intention of placid co-existence sketched out in Genesis 1 was beginning to crystallise on this planet.

But it is not so simple. Jesus himself seems to have been a vigorous carnivore and predator. He evidently ate the lamb at the Passover feast,[31] and gave shrewd and deadly advice on fishing to his disciples.[32] Even after his resurrection, when occupying that resurrection body which was the first visible manifestation of the new, redeemed kingdom of which vegetarianism is evidently a key principle, he stood on a beach cooking fish.[33] The temple in Jerusalem, where Jesus spent a great deal of time, was a vast slaughterhouse, awash with blood and echoing with the grunts and screams of dying animals, and yet Jesus never once denounced the sacrificial system. And what is more, in the most dramatic act of exorcism in the New Testament, he sacrificed a whole herd of pigs in order, apparently, to create a memorable visual aid.[34] St Francis of Assisi, whose proverbial rapport with the animals amazed, inspired and converted, seems in that respect to have embodied the coming kingdom more obviously than the King.

So although Jesus may ultimately turn out to be part of the solution, for the time being at least he is part of the problem.

CHAPTER 8

Vegetarian Lions and Fallen Angels: Solutions to the Ethical Problem

If savagery and cruelty are the expressions of a fundamental law, how evil must be that law, and how deep its discordance with the will of the all-loving Creator revealed by Christ, Who clothes the lilies of the field, and without Whom not one sparrow falls to the ground. If we face the facts candidly, we must admit that no one of us, if he had been in the position of Demiurge, would have created a universe which was compelled by the inner necessity of its being to evolve the cobra, the tarantula, and the bacillus of diphtheria. How then, shall that God, the infinite ardours and pulsations of Whose love bear the same relation to our weak emotions of sympathy and fellow-feeling as the infinity of His wisdom does to our dim and limited knowledge, have done so? The answer can only be that He did not do so; that He did not create such a universe; that, in the words of the most ancient Scriptures of our monotheistic faith, in the beginning 'God saw everything that He had made, and behold, it was very good.' To explain evil in Nature, no less than in man, we are compelled to assume a Fall – a revolt against the will of the Creator, a declension from the beauty and glory which God stamped upon His work at the beginning.

(N.P. Williams,
The Ideas of the Fall and of Original Sin)[1]

157

Is the fall of man a solution?

The knee-jerk response of many Christians to the suffering of the natural world will simply be, 'It's the fault of the fall.' They will then sink back into their actual or metaphorical armchairs, thinking that there is really nothing else to say.

Does Christian doctrine really say that the death and suffering of man and other created things was a consequence of the prototypic humans, Adam and Eve, plucking and eating the forbidden fruit? We look in the next chapter at some of the possible anthropological meanings of the 'fall', but first we need to look back at the Genesis story, and then at the way that it was viewed by the New Testament writers.

Genesis 2 says that there was a garden in a region called Eden. Its geographical boundaries are specified. There is an involved debate about where the description says it was located, and whether the Bible intends to indicate a real place on earth.[2] Whatever the case, it is plain that the garden was not the whole of Planet Earth: it was a small, isolated pocket within it. If you are trying to hold on to the *historical* integrity of the Genesis account, this is important: it means that it is not at all incompatible with Genesis to observe that there was animal death and suffering long before Adam and Eve. The garden may have been a highly atypical little island of harmony surrounded by a crashing sea of predation and enmity.

God planted in the garden 'every tree that is pleasant to the sight and good for food' and 'the tree of life also in the midst of the garden, and the tree of the knowledge of good and evil'.[3] The word translated 'evil' here is much broader in Hebrew. It is better rendered simply as 'bad'.[4] We really have no idea what the 'knowledge of good and bad' means. Does it mean knowledge of the fact that there are two moral classes: good and bad? Does it mean the ability to determine into which of those two classes any particular thing should go? Does it mean detailed knowledge of everything that is good and everything that is bad?

Man was installed as the gardener,[5] and given a very stern injunction: 'You may freely eat of every tree of the garden; but of the tree of the knowledge of good and evil you shall not eat, for in the day that you eat of it you shall die.'[6] There was no prohibition on eating the fruit of the tree of life.

Prompted by the serpent, the woman, newly fashioned from her husband's rib, ate some of the fruit of the forbidden tree that was in the middle of the garden, and gave some to the man. God discovered what had happened, and sought out the couple. They confessed what they had done, cravenly blaming someone or something else first: the man blamed the woman, the woman blamed the snake.[7] Having heard the confessions and the mitigation, God passed sentence:

> The LORD God said to the serpent,
> 'Because you have done this,
>> cursed are you among all animals
>> and among all wild creatures;
> upon your belly you shall go,
>> and dust you shall eat
>> all the days of your life.
> I will put enmity between you and the woman,
>> and between your offspring and hers;
> he will strike your head,
>> and you will strike his heel.'
> To the woman he said,
> 'I will greatly increase your pangs in childbearing;
>> in pain you shall bring forth children,
> yet your desire shall be for your husband,
>> and he shall rule over you.'

> And to the man he said,
> 'Because you have listened to the voice of your wife,
>   and have eaten of the tree
> about which I commanded you,
>   'You shall not eat of it',
> cursed is the ground because of you;
>   in toil you shall eat of it all the days of your life;
> thorns and thistles it shall bring forth for you;
>   and you shall eat the plants of the field.
> By the sweat of your face
>   you shall eat bread
> until you return to the ground,
>   for out of it you were taken;
> you are dust,
>   and to dust you shall return.'[8]

Does this contain a sentence of death? Does it strip man of immortality?

It seems not.

Although the tree of life was in the garden, and was not one of the forbidden trees, apparently the humans had not eaten its fruit. They were not yet immortal. If they had eaten the fruit of the tree of life, it seems that even God would not be able to deprive them of immortality.[9] After passing this sentence, God says, 'See, the man has become like one of us, knowing good and evil; and now, he might reach out his hand and take also from the tree of life, and eat, and live for ever.'[10]

Pausing there: the text is plainly saying that had the couple not eaten the fruit of the tree of the knowledge of good and evil, it would never have occurred to them to eat the fruit of the tree of life. It is only because their new-found knowledge might make them do this that the final part of the sentence is necessary.

'Therefore', the text goes on, 'the LORD God sent him forth from the garden of Eden, to till the ground from which he was taken. He drove out the man; and at the east of the garden of Eden he placed the cherubim, and a sword flaming and turning to guard the way to the tree of life.'[11]

If man had been obedient, then, it seems that he would never have eaten the fruit of the tree of life, and would simply have died in the invariable human way. Returning to the ground from which man was taken[12] seems to be simply a description of what happens – the natural course of events – rather than a part of the sentence.

What about suffering? There is not much in the passage about it. There is a comment about 'enmity' between the snake (plainly, as we have already seen,[13] a natural animal) and men,[14] but the snake is distinguished from the other animals in this respect: God is not saying that the whole natural world will henceforth be constantly at war with man.

The woman is told that her pain in childbearing will be greater *than it would otherwise have been*[15] – thereby clearly asserting that she would in any event have had some pain. I will argue in the next chapter that since the particular pain and danger associated with the birth of human offspring is a consequence of the disproportionately large fetal head, what we have here is a comment on the relationship between the 'fall' of man and increased brain size. Animals tend to pop their fetuses out easily, simply because they are not as clever as we are. There is a very obvious link between the 'knowledge' that resulted from the fall and the pain of an overstretched perineum.

The man's agricultural work is hard, and makes him sweat, but we cannot draw from the passage any implication that his nerve endings did not give him nasty sensations before the fruit was tasted. Yes, the ground was cursed,[16] but can we read into that curse a universal infection of nature, causing natural suffering where there was none before? Hardly: its only apparent effect was on man's ability to extract food from it.[17]

How were these chapters viewed by later thinkers?

The truth is that nothing remotely like the 'traditional' Christian doctrine of the fall was recognised either by Jewish scholars or by the early Church. The expression 'fall' of man appears nowhere in the Bible. Neither the origin nor the transmission of sin are mentioned in the Old Testament.[18] When the fall is mentioned in the Judaism of the first century AD, Adam and Eve tend to be regarded as mischievous, immature little children rather than as terribly evil. Adam is gently mocked for having listened too much to his wife's suggestions. There is no tone of catastrophe. One rabbinic speculation is that the fall made Adam shrink. It gave him a worm's eye view, so distorting his perspective.[19] Evil and sin are attributed either to Satan or demonic beings, or to a 'spirit of evil' within man, to which man succumbs. The Gospels say nothing about the origin or the transmission of sin. The early Church Fathers, while mentioning the fall of man, continue, as their Jewish forebears and contemporaries did, to emphasise man's individual responsibility to resist the temptations that beset him.

Augustine[20] was the author of the doctrine as we recognise it. He had a very unhealthy, unbiblical, essentially Gnostic view of sex, and it coloured much of his thought. For Augustine, lust was the primary corrupter of human nature. Adam's fallenness was, like syphilis, transmitted through the sexual act. For him, this venereally transmitted sin was disastrous: it built a colossal wall between God and even a newborn baby. And all creation was infected too. Augustine's view, although it has been assailed ever since, has proved hugely influential and scarily robust. The early Church fought for its life against Gnosticism; it is still fighting, and the battle is not going well.

While interesting, the rest of the history of the doctrine of the fall is unnecessary for our purposes. We need to look at the doctrine with the New Testament at hand.

The passage that so influenced Augustine was Romans 5:12–21. It is worth setting it out in full:

> Therefore, just as sin came into the world through one man, and death came through sin, and so death spread to all because all have sinned – sin was indeed in the world before the law, but sin is not reckoned when there is no law. Yet death exercised dominion from Adam to Moses, even over those whose sins were not like the transgression of Adam, who is a type of the one who was to come.
>
> But the free gift is not like the trespass. For if the many died through the one man's trespass, much more surely have the grace of God and the free gift in the grace of the one man, Jesus Christ, abounded for the many. And the free gift is not like the effect of the one man's sin. For the judgement following one trespass brought condemnation, but the free gift following many trespasses brings justification. If, because of the one man's trespass, death exercised dominion through that one, much more surely will those who receive the abundance of grace and the free gift of righteousness exercise dominion in life through the one man, Jesus Christ.
>
> Therefore just as one man's trespass led to condemnation for all, so one man's act of righteousness leads to justification and life for all. For just as by the one man's disobedience the many were made sinners, so by the one man's obedience the many will be made righteous. But law came in, with the result that the trespass multiplied; but where sin increased, grace abounded all the more, so that, just as sin exercised dominion in death, so grace might also exercise dominion through justification leading to eternal life through Jesus Christ our Lord.

This is no place to debate the whole theological meaning of

this passage. It is complex and controversial. But three points need to be made.

First, we cannot avoid the conclusion that whatever happened in the garden had some subsequent effect on the humans who followed Adam and Eve.

Second, that effect was 'death'.

Third, the passage actually emphasises individual responsibility: 'sin came into the world through one man, and death came through sin, and so death spread to all *because all sinned*'.[21] The picture is of the 'fall' as a gate. Through that gate entered the dark *possibility* of subsequent transgression. We do not have to transgress, although in practice those wild natures of ours, both created and inflamed by the forbidden fruit, will tragically ensure that we do.

What is the 'trespass' that had such dire consequences? The word Paul uses is a very mild one: *paraptoma* – which generally means an inadvertent slip, one to which no particular moral blame is attached. As to the etymology: *para* means 'across'; *pipto* means 'to fall'. The sense of *paraptoma* is thus of stumbling across a line over which one should not have gone. Paul seems to be writing in the rabbinic tradition which played down the fall in a way that would have outraged Augustine and Ian Paisley. The point he is making is that *any* step outside the bounds that circumscribe the nature of man and his relation to God is dangerous.[22]

What is this 'death' which is a consequence of sin? Is it physical death? It does not say so in Romans 5. Paul contrasts 'death' with 'eternal life'[23] and uses 'condemnation' in the same way that he uses 'death'.[24] So Paul may very well mean simply 'spiritual death' – a reading much more concordant with the Genesis story. Douglas Moo points out that 'Paul frequently uses "death" and related words to designate a "physic-spiritual entity" – "total death", the penalty incurred for sin. Here, then, Paul may focus on physical death as the evidence, the outward manifestation of this total death; or, better, he may simply have in mind this death in both its physical and spiritual aspects.'[25]

Similar arguments apply to one of the New Testament's most difficult passages, 1 Corinthians 15, where we see Paul at his most maddening and magnificent. It is extremely tempting to follow C.S. Lewis who, after an uncharacteristically unilluminating glance at the passage, admitted that it was, for him, 'an impenetrable curtain'[26] and gave up. I will certainly do no better than he did, but ought at least to describe the problem and sketch out a solution.

At first blush, it seems that Paul is asserting that there is a direct connection between physical death and Adam's sin: 'For since death came through a human being, the resurrection of the dead has also come through a human being; for as all die in Adam, so all will be made alive in Christ.'[27] But it is not quite so straightforward. Paul goes on:

> The first man [Adam] was from the earth, a man of dust; the second man [Jesus] is from heaven. As was the man of dust, so are those who are of the dust; and as is the man of heaven, so are those who are of heaven. Just as we have borne the image of the man of dust, we will also bear the image of the man of heaven.
>
> What I am saying, brothers and sisters, is this: flesh and blood cannot inherit the kingdom of God, nor does the perishable inherit the imperishable. Listen, I will tell you a mystery! We will not all die, but we will all be changed, in a moment, in the twinkling of an eye, at the last trumpet.[28]

It is at this point that I tend to lose all patience with Paul and, cross-eyed with confusion, wonder, with Lewis, why God, 'having given [St Paul] so many gifts, withheld from him (what would to us seem so necessary for the first Christian theologian) that of lucidity and orderly exposition'.[29] But Paul is the apostle, and I am not, and so I have to do what I can.

It seems that Paul is asserting what Genesis asserted: if you are of dust, as Adam was, you return to dust. If and only if you are of spirit (a far harder, more solid, more durable material than dust) will you endure. Adam's dust-forged body had no chance of immortality without the transformation that can only happen through Jesus. The death brought through Adam's act (Eve is kindly forgotten) was a spiritual death.

The connection between Adam's sin and the suffering of creation is not made in Romans 5. Indeed, it is not made expressly anywhere. In Romans, in fact, Paul expressly says that nature can tell us something about God: 'Ever since the creation of the world [God's] eternal power and divine nature, invisible though they are, have been understood and seen through the things he has made.'[30]

The nearest the New Testament gets to forging a link between the disobedience in the garden and the predation in the tropical rainforest is in Romans 8:

> The creation waits with eager longing for the revealing of the children of God; for the creation was subjected to futility, not of its own will but by the will of the one who subjected it, in hope that the creation itself will be set free from its bondage to decay and will obtain the freedom of the glory of the children of God. We know that the whole creation has been groaning in labour pains until now.[31]

All this says on the point is that somehow the destiny of the natural world is intertwined with the destiny of man. If it is a comment on the pain, waste and apparent caprice of nature, it is a comment so obscure that it hardly helps us in our inquiry. But the idea of a labouring creation is interesting. It suggests, as Genesis 1 does, that creation itself 'brings forth' new things, and indicates that creation can do more than it has to date been permitted to do. If you want to see the evolutionary process in Romans 8, you can. Creation wants to be something other than it is; it has as yet unfulfilled potential. The main context, though, is apocalyptic. There has been frustration up until now, it says, but wait: it is not always going to be this way.

The notion of the fall, then, does not help to excuse God for the suffering in the natural world. The Bible itself does not assert that there is a connection even between the physical death and suffering of humans and the taking of the forbidden fruit. Still less does it say that the disobedient human teeth in the fruit led to the predatory animal teeth in the night. The most that one can say is that the fall meant that the appointed placators of the turbulent creation became part of the turbulence themselves, and so failed to mitigate some of the horror.

On historical grounds, as we have repeatedly seen, the connection is quite impossible to forge. Some have tried to wriggle out of the difficulty posed by the fact that we live on a huge mound of dead molluscs by talking about the fall somehow having had a retrospective effect. But it simply will not do. It would require, as well as a huge space-time warp, a warp in God's nature. To insert those ancient bones and those dinosaur tumours in the historical record would amount to a sinister tampering with the evidence. The creation, including all the dead bits, is supposed to tell of the glory of God: surely he would not have manipulated it so that we could not read rightly of his glory. C.S. Lewis is curtly dismissive of the fall as an explanation for animal pain, and so should we be:

> The origin of animal suffering could be traced, by earlier generations, to the Fall of man – the whole world was infected by the uncreating rebellion of Adam. This is now impossible,

167

for we have good reason to believe that animals existed long before men. Carnivorousness, with all that it entails, is older than humanity.[32]

We need to look further for an explanation. Any would-be defender of God has to look further for a defence.

Other solutions

By and large, and with some honourable exceptions, biologically educated theistic evolutionists have tended to acknowledge that *the* biological engine is traditional Darwinian natural selection, fuelled by selfishness, and to offer a few observations from their own disciplines which tend to mitigate the ethical magnitude of the problem we have just outlined. But to mitigate is not to exculpate. A speech in mitigation assumes guilt, and is aimed to minimise sentence.

By and large, and with some honourable exceptions, theologically educated theistic evolutionists have tended to couch their attempted defences in language of terrifying opacity. The opacity, for once, is not a consequence of confused thinking. It is a consequence of genuinely complex thoughts expressed, very often, as clearly as they could possibly be. We look briefly at the main ideas. But is it really so complicated?

We suggested in the last chapter that the presence of suffering in the natural world is a real problem for anyone seeking to maintain that God is omnipotent and good. (Of course, if he lacks either of these characteristics, there is no problem at all.) The problem is massively exacerbated if the suffering is somehow intrinsic to the method chosen by or even used by God to produce what we see.

Among those who accept that there is a problem, there are broadly three classes of attempted solution.

First, the whole business is so utterly mysterious that we cannot begin to fathom it.

Second, the suffering is necessary: it is intrinsic to the process, and no other process is possible. The end is good, and there is no other way of reaching it.

Third, the suffering is not necessary in the sense of being intrinsic to the process. It is not demanded by omnipotence. But it is a by-product of a cosmic struggle in which God will ultimately prevail. Omnipotence could produce immediate and decisive victory, but holds off for the time being.

We examine these in turn.

Too mysterious to discuss?

Well, possibly. Certainly in many individual cases of human and animal suffering it will be quite impossible to say, 'This is why it happened . . .' Anyone who posits a straightforward causal relationship between (for instance) human sin and all human pain has read neither Scripture nor the world. I cannot blame any notional Adam directly for my own moral failures, and I can blame neither him nor the sin of anyone else for the existence of childhood leukaemia.[33] Still less can I send the indictment for the whole natural history of the *Ichneumonidae* to his old address somewhere in Mesopotamia.

But the broader questions can at least be debated. We might well finish by throwing up our hands in confusion, but let's not start there.

Necessary?

It is no slight to omnipotence to say that there are some things that even omnipotence cannot do. It cannot make two plus two equal five; it cannot give something to X and at the same time withhold it; it cannot make X (or itself) simultaneously both exist and not exist. It cannot, in other words, do the *intrinsically* impossible.[34]

What goes for ends sometimes and necessarily goes for means. If something is intrinsically necessary to a desired end, omnipotence has to permit it. If the desired end is the number 5, and omnipotence starts with 2, even omnipotence will have to add 3. No other method is possible.

Some have said that the suffering in the natural world is necessary to make it the place that it was designed to be. For some, the quality that the desired world must have, and which justifies the pain, is an aesthetic quality. The world God desires is a picture with a particular tonal quality, said Augustine, borrowing the idea from Plotinus. In order to get the balance right, the dark of pain is necessary as well as the light of well-being. Yes, the dark is dark, but overall the picture is the one that God wants to paint, and therefore good. No other combination of tones would do. You need the pain. Karl Barth thought of creation like a piece of Mozart: there is dissonance, but the dissonance is absolutely necessary to the music, and the dissonance is ultimately resolved.[35]

It seems to me that if God is like that, he is simply not good. Dostoevsky's Ivan is better than he is. Any good person would sacrifice any merely aesthetic harmony to stop the suffering of a child or a baboon. And I think Jesus would.

More potent is the suggestion that pain and suffering are an undesired consequence of there being genuine free will in the creation. If free will is an essential characteristic of the desired universe, then suffering must be possible, and that suffering must include the suffering of non-human creatures. This thesis has been deftly dismantled by Michael Lloyd,[36] and I will not rehearse his arguments. A few points, though.

If the free will being talked about is only human free will, the perspective is crushingly anthropocentric. It is quite impossible to see a necessary connection between the free will of a human and the suffering necessarily inherent (if the Darwinists and only the Darwinists are right) in the evolution of a bank vole. God could presumably have created an entirely free man without any reference at all to bank voles. He could not stop a free man doing nasty things to bank voles, but that is a different matter altogether.

But what if the free will is not merely that of humans? What if free will is somehow inherent (and God wants it to be inherent) in the whole of the created order?

It has to be said that God has a distinct tendency to delegate. He seems to want his creatures to do things for themselves wherever possible. He makes man the gardener, the steward and the subduer, and works through him even when it would appear to be hugely more efficient for God to do everything directly. Apparently he does not delegate only to humans. As we have seen, the planet itself seems to play some real part in birthing the natural world:[37] 'Let the earth put forth vegetation';[38] 'Let the waters bring forth swarms of living creatures';[39] 'Let the earth bring forth living creatures of every kind'.[40] Perhaps this implies real choice on the part of the non-human creation. Perhaps the creation could have chosen not to 'put forth' at all, to 'put forth' something slightly different from that which God intended, or to use a slightly different method from that envisaged? Or perhaps the delegation was total: perhaps God had no formulated intention at all other than the intention to let his creatures do what they like. I have suggested already that there are some subtle but distinct signs that the creation, at the very earliest stages, did indeed have not only the capacity but also the inclination to rebel.[41]

We should not, however, get carried away with this idea. These signs are subtle indeed. If we were meant to draw hugely significant conclusions from them – if cosmic freedom were meant to be a central pillar of our theology – surely the signs would have been more obvious. It is one thing to delegate some real choices to the cosmos, or to live with the free choices of the earth. It is quite another to say that the free will of the cosmos or the earth is so important that it should be able to trump the happiness of individual creatures. Individuals are supposed to matter profoundly. Principles exist for individuals, not individuals for principles. Sabbaths are for men, not men for Sabbaths. Individuals are the point of it all: nothing else can be meant by God's continuous and deafening insistence that *relationship* is what we and all other creatures are designed for. It is impossible to think what might be meant by the free will of something as amorphous as 'the cosmos' or 'the earth'. But it is not at all difficult to imagine the pain of its individual creatures, and surely, however fundamental cosmic freedom is, it must give way, as Ivan and all decent people would want it to give way, to the demands of the bank vole's pain receptors.

Some try to rescue Darwinian evolution from its moral difficulties by saying that free will is inherent in the whole biological struggle; that the struggle is a price we have to pay for the preservation of free will. But while it may make sense to talk about a rabbit making choices that affect its destiny, those choices (so far as we know) have no ethical content at all, and accordingly it seems pointless for free will in the human sense to be concerned about them. Outside the world of Beatrix Potter, animals do not make moral choices. Peter Rabbit was ethically naughty when he disobeyed his mother and went to eat Mr MacGregor's lettuces, but *Oryctolagus cuniculus* is not being morally bad when he gets into the garden. Natural selection might frown and wag its finger if the rabbit gets caught by Mr MacGregor and put into a pie, but there will be no morality anywhere in its judgement. In any event, the *choices* the rabbit makes are not the main thing that determines his destiny. Usually his genes (sometimes acting, it is true, through 'conscious' choices) determine whether he is inside or outside the pie.

It is the presumed inability of animals to make morally meaningful choices, of course, that renders hopelessly inadequate in the realm of animal suffering all the things in the Bible that are supposed to comfort us when faced with the horrible business of human pain. I can see that my own pain might refine me and teach me. But I cannot see that nature, or any of its components, is refined or taught anything edifying by being trampled on, eaten or dismembered.

If we see creatures as instruments of a higher purpose, we turn God into a vivisector. That is the real problem with seeing the Darwinian world as a huge laboratory used by God to test out the vast number of possibilities. This is the view of Alfred North Whitehead's 'process theology'. It is complex, but well summarised by Thomas Hosinksi:

> God acts on the world by organizing and presenting potentials or possibilities. God creates the world by making it possible, by endowing each agent in creation with its potentials and the freedom to create itself on this divinely-given ground. Each agent is free to actualize any of the potentials or possibilities open to it in its situation. The only way God can influence the free self-actualization of each agent is by 'luring' it towards those possibilities God values as most beautiful and good. Thus God acts in the world through persuasion, not through coercion. What finally happens is finally in the hands of the causal agents of the world.
>
> At each moment God experiences what each agent in the universe has chosen to do in its freedom and responds to it by presenting to each agent in the next moment new possibilities for good. In this way God seeks to overcome whatever evils or tragedies have resulted from the exercise of freedom by all agents in the universe.[42]

In process theology, then, there are some real metaphysical constraints on God's action.[43] It is not, as in kenotic thought (to which we will come), that he voluntarily chooses not to exercise his power. It is that to exercise his power to avoid a particular undesirable result would be to ablate the freedom inherent in the world. And since freedom is the point of the world, God cannot do that without changing utterly the nature of the world. It is a classic example of a metaphysical impossibility. Not even omnipotence can have a free world whose free but unfortunate choices are benevolently overruled.

But is there really some moral virtue in letting molecules and genes have the 'freedom' to generate, randomly, endless new combinations? And if there is, does that virtue outweigh the evil of letting natural selection choose brutally between them? If God is omnipotent and omniscient, he presumably knows what DNA configurations will produce 'good' organisms, and has the power to direct them.[44] So why does he not do it? The 'free will' of the organisms themselves (if we can talk meaningfully about the 'free will' of non-human animals or plants) is not violated by only the 'good' sorts being created.

According to Whitehead, God is experiencing at each moment everything that his creatures are experiencing. This is partly a philosophical necessity – a consequence of the inherence of the universe in God. But mostly it is to make God look better: to make it look as if he is not getting away pain-free while causing or permitting his creatures to suffer. Peacocke writes:

> The ubiquity of pain, predation, suffering and death as the means of creation through biological evolution entails, for any concept of God to be morally acceptable and coherent, that we cannot but tentatively propose that God suffers in, with, and under the creative processes of the world with their costly unfolding in time.[45]

It is a curious defence. Imagine that X sets a house on fire. There is a family in the house. X stays in the house while it is blazing, and indeed finds the family and stays in the same room with them as they are all cremated. Is X less guilty of the crimes of arson and murder because he stayed in the house?

In the Whitehead model, God is on the side both of the hunter and the hunted. He experiences the hunger of the lioness and the fear of the wildebeest as it is separated from the herd and brought down by the lioness. Is it too irreverent to say sarcastically on behalf of the wildebeest, 'Thanks *so* much for identifying with me in that obscure metaphysical way. It really made a difference when my udder was ripped and my neck dislocated'? Back in the burning house: how much comfort is it to the family to have X there with them?

The process thinkers recognise this difficulty, and some of them think that it can only be solved by postulating another life for the wildebeest, in which its frustrated potential can be realised.[46]

A similar theme of profound identification between God and the suffering creature is found in the notion of *kenosis*, which sees creation as cruciform. Again, we need not explore the burgeoning literature of kenotic thought, but we should note that its cornerstone text is the famous passage from Philippians which talks about Christ:

> who, though he was in the form of God,
>   did not regard equality with God
>   as something to be exploited,
> but emptied himself,
>   taking the form of a slave,
>   being born in human likeness.
> And being found in human form,
>   he humbled himself

> and became obedient to the point of death –
> even death on a cross.[47]

This extraordinary divine condescension, say the kenotic thinkers, extends to God becoming the slave of the forces of natural selection. He suffers with the frog as it is eaten by the snake, and somehow that suffering is redemptive. The Philippians passage does not end with suffering and abasement. Suffering and abasement are the route to glory. It goes on: 'Therefore God also highly exalted him and gave him the name that is above every name.'[48]

God, in kenotic thought, is like a father who wants his children to grow up, and so does not direct them as much as might at first seem necessary. He chooses to limit the exercise of his power in the world. He is almighty God, but for the moment what is most visibly almighty about him is his love and his suffering, not his power.[49]

This is poetic, intoxicating, and very useful for anyone trying to build bridges between Western Christian thought and the wisdom of the East, but is it really a solution to the problem posed? It is better than the process thinkers' suggestion, because kenosis goes somewhere: redemption is at the end of the road. Suffering is meaningful; it counts; it is not all wasted. But kenosis assumes that the suffering was necessary in the first place. And that has yet to be demonstrated.

Let's go back to the burning house and suppose X is a mustard-keen kenoticist. He says to the cowering family, now covered in terrible burns: 'It'll all be all right in the end, you know. The fact that I'm suffering with you means that your suffering is particularly significant,[50, 51] and since I'm a redeemer figure I'll make sure that you look back on this as a useful step on the way to glory.' The metaphor is a limited one, of course. One might well imagine that the human family could benefit spiritually from a nasty experience. But what about a fawn caught in a forest fire?

The family's likely response would be: 'Well, thank you for the promise of rescue. It is appreciated. But wouldn't it have been far better if you hadn't set the house on fire in the first place?' The only possible response from X is: 'It was necessary to set the house on fire. This wasn't rescue for rescue's sake.' Which brings us right back to the basic question: Could creation have been set up in a way that did not necessarily involve animal suffering? Most kenotic theories are not wrong; they just do not do what they are often said to do. They do not begin to explain why suffering is necessary.

Two major kenotic thinkers, Holmes Rolston III and Arthur Peacocke, have grasped the nettle.[52] They seem to me to be badly stung by it. They see pain and suffering as an inevitable corollary of sentience, and sentience as an inevitable corollary of life. The more complex an organism is, the greater will be its capacity for both pain and pleasure. Take away the capacity for pain, and you take away the capacity for joy. Lithium might reduce the depth of the trough into which a manic-depressive falls; it also lops off the ecstatic, manic peaks. Life is basically, and inevitably, like lithium. Euthanasia is really the only way to take away pain. Death itself is necessary for life: you are assembled from parts previously used by now-dead organisms. The space in the universe I occupy was previously occupied by something or someone else. There is not room for both of us. I am necessarily parasitic on others; their death is my life. I cannot live to praise God unless someone has died to allow it, and accordingly it is churlish as well as unscientific to blame him for their death.

It is at this point that the scientifically educated theistic evolutionists start to contribute. I have already said that their offerings tend to be speeches in mitigation.

In response to the observation that natural selection involves a lot of waste, they reply that on a merely biological level, the organisms cast into the dustbin of natural selection are not wasted at all: their bodies will be quickly assimilated into other living bodies.[53] Anyway, what is waste? What is and is not waste will depend on what the craftsman was trying to do. Perhaps those tens of thousands of newly hatched mayflies that gusted within seconds of emergence into the water had all the fulfilment that they could possibly have desired; all the pleasure and significance for which they were designed. And on other levels, who knows? Perhaps any unfulfilled potential will be realised in another life.

In response to the observation that there seems to be an awful lot of death around, they reply that since the observed mortality rate for living organisms is exactly 100 per cent (or arguably not quite 100 per cent, because there was a single bizarre exception, and even he should perhaps be counted because his death appears to have been a pretty regular human death), the amount of death in the world precisely equals the amount of life in the world.

In response to the suggestion that, even if pain is necessary, its intensity seems to be unnecessarily high, they reply that this is not the case. If our pain receptors were rather slower to fire off in the first place, or fired off at a lower rate when they were activated, we would apparently be less safe than we are. And they comment that there are some efficient pain-control systems. God does not leave the natural world without analgesia. Yes, pain is necessary, but God does his best, within the constraints set by the only possible designs, to minimise that pain.

When a painful stimulus occurs, cells at the base of our spinal cord release natural opiates into our bloodstream. Break your leg, and you are immediately on heroin. It is not at all obvious how natural selection might produce such benevolent systems.

Vegetarian Lions and Fallen Angels

Large predators often use relatively kind means of killing – often biting through the relatively poorly innervated neck skin and dividing the carotid artery and the jugular vein, so causing a rapid drop in blood pressure and a speedy loss of consciousness.[54] They are fond of quoting David Livingstone's account of his near-death experience in the jaws of an African lion, and they endorse his theological conclusions:

> The shock produced a stupor ... It caused a sort of dreaminess in which there was no sense of pain nor feeling of terror ... This peculiar state is probably produced in all animals killed by Carnivora; and, if so, is a merciful provision by our benevolent Creator for lessening the pain of death.[55]

I do not intend to mock these thoughts, or to diminish the significance of the observations. They are useful thoughts and highly significant observations. It is just that, again, I cannot see that they begin to amount to a justification of the animal suffering that we see. After reading everything that the process thinkers and the kenotic theorists have to say, I go back to the tangled bank and become fearful and doubtful again. Their theories seem so anthropocentric and anthropomorphic. They credit animals with a capacity for joy which is linked to their capacity for pain in a way algebraically similar to the way those two capacities are linked in humans. I can see no evidence for that linkage.

I do not doubt that animals do things merely for pleasure; I do not at all doubt that they have joys of a sort. No one who has watched swifts diving gratuitously around rooftops, in a way that makes no thermodynamic sense, no evolutionary sense, but a great deal of sheer fun sense, could possibly doubt it. But I doubt very much indeed that the potential proportions of joy and misery in the swifts are anything like those of a human. The swifts are oppressed by the stern regime of natural selection in a far more direct way than we are. Natural selection polices its regime with diligence and brutality. It is not completely true to say that a swift's life is nothing but nasty, brutish and short, but it is a massively more accurate approximation than the same comment about a human life. In relative terms there is a lot more misery in an animal life, and accordingly it is not possible to excuse the misery simply by saying, 'If it didn't have the nastiness it wouldn't have the joy either.' Any prudent swift would happily trade its limited store of joy for relief of the heavy burden imposed on it by natural selection.

Even in our own lives, it is not necessary actually to suffer pain in order to experience joy. The most joyful people are not always those who have had the most unpleasant time. If the potential to suffer is a necessary corollary of the potential to have joy, could omnipotence not easily have rigged the system so that the ratio of *actual* joy to pain was far greater than it is? What vital principles or potentialities would have been torpedoed by such benevolence?

Accordingly we are forced back to the conclusion that all the horror of the tangled bank is indeed bad, and that the only possible defence for God is that he did not want it that way and is not responsible for it being that way.

We have seen already that God does not seem to smile on all the stuff used as the fuel of the Darwinian engine. He did not want or intend predation, and looks forward to a time when it will not happen. He does not shrug his shoulders at death, saying, as I have parodied the theistic evolutionists as saying, 'That's just the way it's meant to be. Death's just a part of life.' He thinks it is obscene, weeps at the death of Lazarus, and says that his mission is to put death to death. He does not say about disease, 'You plainly don't have the genes necessary to avoid that illness, and it's a good thing that natural selection has found you out before you transmit them to the next generation.'

He stalks around Palestine incontinently weeping and incontinently healing.

If God is not responsible for the design and behaviour of the *Ichneumonidae*, then who or what is?

The answer, at one level, is of course that natural selection appears to be responsible. We must remember that the *Ichneumonidae* are in many ways beautiful and wondrous things. Nature is at least as green in tooth and claw as it is red. We cannot and should not propose that natural selection is only a tool of demons, producing only abomination. The problem for anyone who believes in a good and powerful God involved in creation is not that he chose to use natural selection, but that both the by-products and the end-products of natural selection seem to contain *elements* antithetical to the picture of God that orthodox Christianity paints. Nature is a weird, heady cocktail of splendour, horror, joy and agony: we would like it to be made out of pure God-juice.

It is worth observing that some of the things that have worried us so far about natural selection's methods (and in particular pain and predation) are not logically necessary to its operation – although of course they happen in fact, and are used powerfully. Death is only necessary when the supply of available ecological niches becomes utterly exhausted, or the pool of available resources for body-construction is so depleted that no more bodies can be built without recycling some existing ones. The only element necessarily intrinsic to natural selection that we most certainly cannot reconcile with the character of the self-giving Galilean is the psychotic individualism of natural selection; the relentless selfishness; the fact that organisms clamber always over the bodies of others (whether or not the bodies are dead). Natural selection starts all its sentences with 'I want'; Christianity starts all its sentences with 'What do you want?'

What this mixed-up-ness of the nature cocktail means is that when we are hunting the criminal behind the *Ichneumonidae*, we are not looking for a creator or an innovator. Even having looked hard at the natural world, and discounted the fall of man as a suspect, we can continue to accept the basic traditional Christian view of nature – that it is an essentially good thing twisted.

The criminal – the twister – will have the following characteristics.

He will be immensely ancient: he will have been around to inject selfishness into the primordial soup. As soon as it is palaeontologically possible to see his footprints, we will see them.

He will oppose the rule of God, be the antithesis of God's character, and be the inciter of the rebellion whose traces we see in Genesis 1 and 2. It was his voice whispering seductively to the earth, 'Don't grass grass; do your own thing.' It was his work that needed to be subdued by man. He may not have been the snake in the garden, but he was its inspiration and perverter. He gave Noah his illegitimate taste for flesh, and made carnivores unclean to the priests of Israel. He fumes if a wolf lies peaceably down beside a lamb.

Some have called him nature itself, or the forces of free will inherent in nature.[56] We have examined the problems with that thesis.

N.P. Williams, cited earlier, suggests that there was a 'collective fall of the race-soul of humanity in an indefinitely remote past'.[57] This Jungian language will appeal instinctively to many, but why put humanity or anything involving humanity's primordial 'race-soul' into the frame at all for crimes which occurred billennia before the first man rose tentatively onto his hind legs? It is true that we are linked directly to the first organisms by our shared DNA – Dawkins's 'River flowing out of Eden' – and it is interesting and not necessarily biologically absurd to speculate that trapped within our double helices is some primeval race-memory of the time when our ancestors were bacteria. But memory is not culpability. To say that the agent of the fall is for that reason somehow human is counter-intuitive and odd. It would make more biological sense to say that it was a bacterial race-soul.

There is one suspect who fits the description very well. Christian and Jewish tradition talks about a dark figure of uncertain origins but great antiquity: a fallen angel.[58] C.S. Lewis again:

> It is impossible at this point not to remember a certain sacred story which, though never included in the creeds, has been widely believed in the Church and seems to be implied in several Dominical, Pauline and Johannine utterances – I mean the story that man was not the first creature to rebel against the Creator, but that some older and mightier being long since became apostate and is now the emperor of darkness and (significantly) the Lord of this world ... It seems to me, therefore, a reasonable supposition, that some mighty created power had already been at work for ill on the material universe, or the solar system, or, at least, the planet Earth, before ever man came on the scene; and that when man fell, someone had, indeed, tempted him ... If there is such a power, as I myself believe, it may well have corrupted the animal creation before man appeared.[59]

The notion of corruption is important. This being – this corrupter – was itself a creature, and could not create. It can sour the fresh milk of creation, it can produce ulcers on an already created body, it can make cells run haywire and make cancers. But although it can turn a smile to a grimace, it cannot produce the face that does both.

We can rejoice in the *Ichneumonidae* up to a point. We can admire the basic blueprint, but regret that coffee has been spilled over it by a malevolent hand.

Could God have stopped the corruption? We must presume that he could. If he had stopped it, would he also have stopped the world from being one in which animals and plants could thrive? Would he have snatched away their raison d'être – the relationship with one another and with God for which they were apparently called out of non-existence? Unless free will is in some way grafted into the non-human creation in ways that we can neither see nor imagine, it is hard to see that stopping the nastiness would have frustrated the whole purpose of creation. As far as we can see, stopping nastiness would simply have stopped nastiness. As soon as man bursts onto the scene, brandishing his moral consciousness, things are very different. His freedom necessitates the possibility of evil: nothing before him obviously did.

If God could have excised this primordial cancer from the creation without free will being at stake, why did he not do it? We do not know. We are given no hints. All that we can say is that because he is love, he loathes it; because he is peace, he is at war with it; because he is ingenious, he can bring good things even out of bad; because he is almighty, he will ultimately triumph over it.

God's Genesis 1 dream of harmony in the creation was not just a dream: it was a plan. He put man in charge of the plan. But man the gardener was expelled from the garden; man the subduer needed to be subdued; man the counter-revolutionary became a revolutionary. Instead of being part of the solution, man became part of the problem. It was all tragically predictable. And indeed it had been predicted. In some unimaginable way, the solution had been foreshadowed: the solution to the bloodshed was blood. The way to make lions safe to lambs was to kill a Lamb. And so it was: Revelation talks about the 'Lamb that was slain from the creation of the world'.[60]

On a rubbish tip sometime in the first century AD, an obscure

Jew was nailed to a piece of wood and died. His last words, according to one writer, were, 'It is finished.'[61] It was an eerie echo of another biblical finishing: 'God finished the work that he had done.'[62]

The Christians say that the echo is significant – that the Jew's squalid death marked and effected a new creation; that a creation brought into existence by the words of God was renewed and remade by the death of the enfleshed Word of God.

Three days later, something very strange happened. The Jew, who had been most emphatically dead, appeared again. This time he was most emphatically alive. In fact, he was more alive than anyone had ever been before. His body seems to have been more solid than the ground it walked on. It passed through walls as if through air. It was the very first sample of the type of more-than-but-not-less-than physical matter of which the newly fashioned creation will be made.

To put to rest once and for all any suggestion of smug remoteness from creaturehood and pain, God became part of his creation. It was an intimacy with creation – a solidarity with it – hugely greater than that in the constructs of the process theodicists. God entered the evolutionary chain, and was ultimately a victim of it. In becoming man, he took on our ancestry. God became familiarly related to those ancient bacteria. How otherwise could he redeem them? How else could the anguish of the natural selective process be adequately dealt with? He, who was there at creation, held the stars in his hands and wove the double helix, gave up all power and died young, like those mayflies. He was crushed. The crushing was like the death of any powerless thing, and in a sense *was* the death of *all* of them. He chose not to resist the forces of selection, and by that choice, to the immense surprise and dismay of the ancient adversary, annihilated them. The cross looked like pain, waste and despair – all the things that sickened us when we looked at what natural selection does on the tangled bank. In fact, it was the end of them.

Or at least it was the end of them in a sense. Their end is assured, but their defeated troops will continue to fight on for a while. But there will come a time, we are told, when Isaiah's vision will crystallise on the tangled bank.

The story started in a garden. The Bible is not artistically symmetrical: it ends its story in a city. Since Eden there has been progress. Important things have happened. The object is not simply to restore Eden. The plan is more exciting than that. In the final chapter of the final book of the Bible, we see again the tree of life. It bows down with fruit; its leaves 'are for the healing of the nations'.[63] The old Genesis curse has been lifted. So have all curses. 'Nothing accursed will be found there any more.'[64] There is no death here. Mourning, crying and pain are no more.[65]

Are there animals here? Of course there are. They will be there because there are animals on earth, and the earth persists. Do not bother listening to any speculations about whether animals go to heaven. This is not heaven. Animals do not go to heaven, and neither do we. It cannot be said too often or too strongly that Christians *do not believe that when they die they go to heaven*. The origins of that anaemic doctrine are old and Gnostic, and were unhelpfully entrenched by Plato, Dante and Michelangelo's *Last Judgement*.[66] The consistent teaching of the New Testament is that after death we go for a while into an intermediate state, until Jesus comes *here*, to marry heaven and earth in a new creation. The dying Jesus said to the repentant thief, 'Today you will be with me in paradise.'[67] But Jesus himself was not raised for three days. The 'paradise' Jesus was talking about must have been the intermediate state – something very different from the 'new heaven and new earth' in which our ultimate destinies lie.

You have to hate the body very much (as of course the Gnostics did) to think that a bodiless eternity on a cloud is what we were designed and destined for. God loves his creation. He loves *matter*. Despite all the trouble it has given him, he has not thrown it away and started again, and he never will. The incarnation of God in Jesus is God's affirming 'yes' to the flesh.[68] Jesus' resurrection body – the first example of the sort of body which we will all ultimately have, and which is necessary to allow us to experience the super-sensual, super-material world we will inhabit – was far more material than ours. It related to matter on this earth much as our bodies relate to mist. So keen is God on the material, that the plan for the cosmos is to make it even more material than it currently is.

The plan is not to scrap the earth, but to unite it with heaven in a way so intimate that the only metaphor the Bible can think of is marriage – one-fleshness.[69, 70] In a marriage, the parties do not cease to have their individual natures; the context in which those natures are expressed changes. And so the earth will retain its nature too – a nature inextricably interwoven with and dependent on the living organisms that are here. Animals will be in the new creation because they were a good part of the old. There is a vital continuity between this world and the next[71] – which is one reason why being here is useful preparation for what is to come, and one reason why it matters what we do to this planet. The great prayer in Revelation is 'Come, Lord Jesus',[72] not 'Take, Lord Jesus'. It is 'Come and put right what is wrong *here*', not 'Take us away from this irredeemably wretched place and put us in a place which is more spiritual'.

Since the earth will survive and be glorified, so will its creatures: 'through [Jesus] God was pleased to reconcile to himself *all things*'.[73] If, and in so far as, an anteater needs to be redeemed, it will be. The reconciliation here is a reconciliation not just between God and his creatures, but between the creatures too.

Here is Dostoevsky's Ivan:

With my pitiful, earthly, Euclidian understanding, all I know is that there is suffering and that there are none guilty; that cause follows effect, simply and directly; that everything flows and finds its level – but that's only Euclidian nonsense, I know that, and I can't consent to live by it! What comfort is it to me that there are none guilty and that cause follows effect simply and directly, and that I know it? – I must have justice, or I will destroy myself. And not justice in some remote infinite time and space, but here on earth, and that I could see myself. I have believed in it. I want to see it, and if I am dead by then, let me rise again, for if it all happens without me, it will be too unfair. Surely I haven't suffered simply that I, my crimes and my sufferings, may manure the soil of the future harmony for somebody else. I want to see with my own eyes the hind lie down with the lion and the victim rise up and embrace his murderer. I want to be there when everyone suddenly understands what it has all been for.[74]

If Christianity is true, perhaps he will be there.

CHAPTER 9

The Ape in the Image:
Human Evolution and the Book of Genesis

Placed on the isthmus of a middle state,
A being darkly wise, and rudely great:
With too much knowledge for the sceptic side,
With too much weakness for the stoic's pride,
He hangs between; in doubt to act, or rest;
In doubt to deem himself a god, or beast;
In doubt his mind or body to prefer;
Born but to die, and reasoning but to err ...
Created half to rise, and half to fall;
Great lord of all things, yet a prey to all;
Sole judge of truth, in endless error hurl'd:
The glory, jest and riddle of the world!
(Alexander Pope, *Essay on Man*)[1]

What is man, that thou art mindful of him?
(Psalm 8:4 KJV)

It is no denigration at all of the Neanderthals and of other now-extinct humans – whose attainments were entirely admirable in their own ways – to say that, with the arrival on earth of symbol-centered, behaviourally modern *Homo sapiens*, an entirely new order of being had materialised on the scene. And explaining just how this extraordinary new phenomenon came about is at the same time the most intriguing question, and the most baffling one, in all of biology.

(Ian Tattersall, *The Monkey in the Mirror*, p. 141)

About three and a half million years ago, a group of thirteen small chimp-like creatures (a mixed bunch of adult males and females) clustered together in a ravine running through the savannah of the Afar region in Ethiopia. It was an unwise choice, for heavy rain clouds were gathering. The more alert of them probably heard a rumble moving towards them, or felt the stones higher up the valley shift, but there was no time for them to move before the flash flood hit them. They were buried together under the silt, and there, in 1975, they were discovered by an international expedition.

If they had been able to run from the engulfing water, they would have run on their hind legs, as their knees, their pelvises and the Laetoli footprints show. They were *Australopithecus afarensis*, members of the same species as the famous 'Lucy'. Lucy, the first of their kind to be found, had been unearthed in the previous year by Professor Donald Johanson and his student Tom Gray. As they searched for animal bones, they saw a tiny bone fragment sticking out of a slope. Johanson immediately realised that it was from a hominid. All around were more bones, 47 in all, almost 40 per cent of the whole skeleton. As Johanson and his team were celebrating back in camp, 'Lucy in the Sky with Diamonds' was blasting out of the tinny tape player, and the name Lucy stuck.[2]

As we now reconstruct things, Lucy was on a fairly recently budded twig of a very shabby evolutionary bush. The roots of that tree went all the way down to the bacteria of the primordial slime. The bud had sprung out of the old apes of Africa. Lucy's twig would grow into a branch which would itself branch many times, but at the end of which would ultimately perch a strange thing: an almost hairless biped with a relatively huge head, long hind limbs (good for loping across his native savannah and seeing long distances over the long grass),[3] an opposable thumb (making him a good tool-maker) and an unusual voice box (allowing him to talk, but making it possible for him to choke to death).

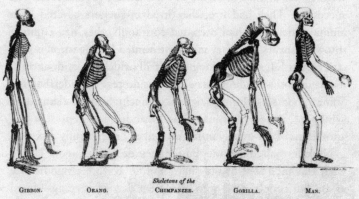

GIBBON. ORANG. *Skeletons of the* GORILLA. MAN.
CHIMPANZEE.

Photographically reduced from Diagrams of the natural size (except that of the Gibbon, which was twice as large as nature), drawn by Mr. Waterhouse Hawkins from specimens in the Museum of the Royal College of Surgeons.

Man's place in nature. *Frontispiece to T. H. Huxley's* Evidence as to Man's Place in Nature *(1863).*

This biped was sociable and co-operative. His powers of co-operation were used in and fuelled by his hunting of large and dangerous animals. This curious ape had a passion for art, an interest in his own death and the death of other members of his species and, oddly, he seemed to believe in his own immortality.

He was called *Homo sapiens*. When he finally blossomed, the earth had seen nothing like him. But he took a long time to blossom. Fascinating though the story of his eventual take-off is, the story of his extraordinary stasis is even stranger and more puzzling.

When anatomically modern *Homo sapiens* first appeared, they shared the earth with the Neanderthals (*Homo neanderthalensis*), who had a wide distribution throughout Europe and West Asia from more than two hundred thousand years ago to about twenty-seven thousand years ago. Neanderthals were, by the standards of the day, immensely sophisticated and successful. They had fire, they lived in shelters covered with animal hides, they had prepared-core tools, they had cunning throwing spears, and they may have hunted (the question is very contentious). If they had language at all (which is very doubtful), it was doubtless rudimentary. There is no real Neanderthal art. Some crude scratchings have unconvincingly been claimed as symbols.[4] Tattersall thinks that Neanderthals represent the apotheosis of the merely intuitive thinker. I respectfully disagree.

Neanderthals sometimes buried their dead, but no one is sure what this indicated. It may have had no symbolic significance at all, but simply have been a prudent way of keeping human carrion out of their noses, out of their shelters, and away from the unwanted attention of dangerous scavengers. If it was a way of dealing with feelings of loss, that is in itself no reason to infer any belief in the numinous or any afterlife.

Those who say that there is evidence of Neanderthal spirituality rely on two finds from the Shanidar cave in the Zagros mountains of northern Iraq. The first is the skeleton of a man who was forty years old, or even more – very old indeed for his day. He had healed head injuries and a withered arm. The arm injury was old, and may have been congenital. Here, say the proponents, is a suggestion that Neanderthals were not savagely utilitarian: they clearly valued something in that old man that was not merely physical. His survival to old age implies some sort of social care, and that implies that they had their eyes on something other than where the next meal was coming from.

The second find from Shanidar is even more interesting. It is the notorious 'flower-burial'. A Neanderthal man lies in a grave rich in the pollen of spring flowers. Does this mean that he lay on a bed of flowers, or had flowers placed deliberately on his body? If it does, it is the only convincing evidence of Neanderthal grave goods, and it would allow some meaningful speculation about Neanderthal attitudes towards death. The excavator of the site, Ralph Solecki, thought that the type of pollen found was significant. Many of the flowers, he said, 'are known to have herbal properties and are used by the people of the region today . . . One may speculate that Shanidar IV was not only a very important man, a leader, but also may have been a kind of medicine man or shaman in his group.' But interpretation of the find is extremely difficult. Tattersall and Schwartz note that 'various post-depositional processes, such as the burrowing of rodents, can produce a similar result'.[5]

Whatever these finds mean, there is no debate about one thing: almost as soon as behaviourally modern, symbol-manipulating *Homo sapiens* arrive in a neighbourhood, Neanderthals disappear. But here is the important thing: that crucially modern *behaviour* arrived much later than the hardware which is necessary and apparently sufficient for that behaviour. We return shortly to this curious fact.

The overwhelming consensus is that *Homo sapiens* evolved in Africa and spread outwards – the 'Out of Africa' theory.[6] In 2003, the Awash area of Ethiopia yielded a significant find, a morphologically *almost* modern human, about one hundred and sixty thousand years old, and christened *Homo sapiens idaltu* – The Elder Thinking Man. We do not know when, morphologically, he first shed his entitlement to the *idaltu*, and became truly morphologically modern, but we can say confidently that by a hundred thousand years ago at the very latest there were, in Africa and the Levant, humans who were skeletally more or less identical to us.

They were not, however, the same in other ways. Behaviourally they were very different. One of the first places that we see this is in Israel, and we see it there because they showed a talent for co-existence with other races that vanished with the explosive emergence of modern us.

Men are walkers. The first place outside Africa that these ancient *Homo sapiens* got to was the Levant, which they reached at least a hundred thousand years ago. They did not drive out the local Neanderthals. They may have stayed in the Levant, happily co-existing with the Neanderthals for the next sixty thousand years; or they may, for some reason, have died out in the Levant or retreated back to Africa. But the important thing is that the Neanderthals stayed.[7] No fully modern man has ever tolerated a rival species for long at all.

The absence of genocide is not the only marker of behavioural non-modernity. Although these Levantine *Homo sapiens* did bury their dead with apparently some sort of ritual (many of the bones at the Qafzeh cave, near Nazareth, where these ancient humans have been found, are stained with red ochre, and there are various grave goods, including the mandible of a wild boar placed in the arms of one of the skeletons), their ritual behaviour and culture were rudimentary compared to what happened at the dramatic dawn of the Upper Palaeolithic. They show none of the emphatic, vibrant symbolising. Their lives, so far as we can reconstruct them, were very similar to those of the Neanderthals.

The last of the Levantine Neanderthals rests at about the same geologic levels in which appear the first traces of behaviourally modern *Homo sapiens*. About forty-five thousand years ago, Upper Palaeolithic culture dawned in the Levant, and as soon as it did, the Neanderthal sun, which had shone so promisingly for so long, sank below the horizon, never to rise again. We see the same in Europe.[8] The Neanderthals did not long survive the advent of this culture there. They hung on for a while, perhaps persisting longest in remote parts of the Iberian peninsula. And then they disappear there too.

We do not know precisely why they disappeared. We do not know whether they were peaceably marginalised, genetically swamped or ethnically cleansed. But however it happened, the first visible effect of *Homo sapiens* on another related species is genocide.

The explosion into the world of these strange, modern men-from-nowhere was not just a population explosion, not mere biological success. It was an explosion of sensibility.[9] The Upper Palaeolithic shelves at the museums are crowded with votive objects, sculptures, wind instruments and kiln-baked ceramics.[10] These early moderns clearly felt that the everyday business of life had a significance other than simple survival, for they celebrated it. They decorated tediously functional items such as scraper handles, and did not see their bodies as tediously functional, since they beautified them with necklaces, bracelets and pendants.

They organised, divided and classified their world. They may have had lunar calendars, and certainly kept tallies of some things with notches on bone catalogues.[11] They had no doubt named the animals, and they drew beautiful colour pictures of them on rock walls, but their relationship with the animals seems to have been more intimate than that of a simple taxonomist. Their paintings show a true empathetic and sympathetic entry into the animals' world. They did not simply observe: they expounded.

They were highly social, well organised and co-operative. They transported tool-making materials long distances, had sophisticated factories (which probably implies trade), and probably (unlike the Neanderthals) brought large animals to a central depot for butchering and sharing.

When they died, their bodies were often arrayed in great splendour and at great cost. They plainly thought that they were going somewhere, and would need material things there. Thirty thousand years ago, at Sungir, not far from Moscow, three Upper Palaeolithic humans (an elderly man and two children) were buried with extraordinary riches. Their clothes were decorated with, between them, more than thirteen thousand ivory beads, each of which probably took more than an hour to make. On his forearms and biceps the man wore twenty-five mammoth-ivory bracelets, around his neck was a painted schist pendant, and a bead cap containing fox teeth was on his head. The children wore similar headdresses, and they also had bone rings, chest plaques, fox-teeth belts, ivory pendants carved in the shape of a mammoth, and various other grave goods including a lance made from a straightened mammoth tusk. Whatever sort of economy these people had, this was a lavish burial. They obviously did not think that to put hundreds of thousands of dollars in the permafrost was a waste.

What was it that gave these early modern men such a distinct and devastating edge over the Neanderthals? Whatever it was, it was not sheer brain size. Neanderthals, in fact, tended to have rather larger brains than *Homo sapiens*. No new brain parts were bolted on: not much had happened to the basic design of the brain, indeed, for several millions of years. The brain's layout is remarkably uniform among all the higher primates. We simply cannot account for the functional differences between early moderns and Neanderthals just by looking at their brains.

Many answers have been proposed. Memes and the ability to imitate, say some;[12] religion, mysticism,[13] or mental time travel[14] say others. Ian Tattersall, who is well worth listening to, writes, 'Lately . . . I've begun to believe that if there is one single feature of human beings that accounts for – or at least correlates nicely with – their often bizarre behaviours, it is a simple intolerance of boredom. Think about it: it could account for a lot.'[15]

Yet there is one outstanding characteristic which blazes out

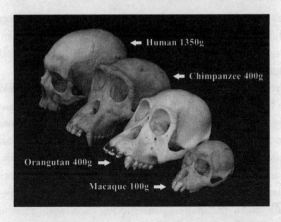

Primate skulls and typical brain weights. From Molecular Insights into Human Brain Evolution, *Jane Bradbury, PLoS Biology Vo. 3(3). Primate skulls from the Museum of Comparative Zoology, Harvard.*

of the records we have, and on which all the other suggestions could well be parasitic. Modern man had an unprecedented ability to see the world in the form of symbols. Of all the things his vast brain had given him, this was the greatest: he could ask himself, 'What if?' It gave him an immense selective advantage. He could sit around his fire (for fire-making was another of his skills) and experiment in his mind with endless possibilities. He could remake the world in his imagination, and test out the various combinations he had invented. His brain became a laboratory in which he could analyse the consequences of various actions or inactions. These cognitive dry runs were a lot safer than trying out his schemes for the first time in the real world of bears and grudge-bearing clansmen.

Perhaps this cognitive ability was a by-product of language, for words, after all, are the most potent of symbols. Or maybe language burst out of his brain, perhaps as a result of the pent-up pressure of all that symbolising. Perhaps his head would have exploded had the faculty not been channelled and system-atised. Certainly, once language had emerged, language and the basic capacity to symbolise prodded one another synergistically to greater feats.

A creature with such a busy head is bound to get bored sitting where he is. A cave will quickly become dull for someone who can imagine other things. Symbols generate discontent, and discontent generates movement, innovation, exploration and ambition. If it is not the father of a theory of mind, symbolism is at least a sibling. Symbols allow the 'I' of a developed consciousness to go travelling, and therefore to develop further. Symbols allow the mental construction of a world in which 'I' do not exist, and accordingly prompt meditation on my own death. Where no obvious causes exist, symbols can supply them. Where obvious causes are at odds with a symbolically erected world view which is generally more congenial than the everyday world, symbols can magic up more convenient causes – hence religion, say the sceptics.

We now have to go back to the strange business of the struc-turally modern but behaviourally old *Homo sapiens* of Africa and the Levant.

The eruption of the behavioural moderns is so abrupt, so dramatic in the archaeological record and so tectonic in its effects on everything around them that it has been argued that the eruption is actually a new, explosive speciation event. Ian Tattersall, along with most other mainstream anthropologists, dismisses the idea:

The time frame doesn't appear to permit it. For this explana-tion to work, a new human species, physically identical but intellectually superior to one that already existed, would have had to appear and then to spread throughout the Old World in a remarkably short space of time, totally eliminating its predecessor species in the process. And there is no indication at all, in an admittedly imperfect record, that anything of this kind occurred.[16]

Assuming that it is right to dismiss the idea of a new species, what could have happened? What could have been the trigger for the sudden emergence, using only the existing wiring, of whatever it is that makes humans human?

When all is said, this remains a wholly baffling mystery. To observe (as is very obviously true) that symbolism and language would give an enormous selective advantage is to compound the problem, not to solve it. We have noted already that to say that something would be useful is a very different thing from giving an account of its origins. The neurological and laryngeal equipment necessary for language and symbolisation was present in those early Levantine *Homo sapiens*-who-weren't-particularly-*sapiens*, and under those intense selective pressures one would expect to see the incremental (but quite speedy) emergence of modern behaviour. But we do not. It is enough to make anthropologists get theological, and that is what we are going to do next.

We have already had a brief look at what Genesis says about the genesis and the 'fall' of man. The main purpose of that look was to note that man's disobedience did not explain suffering and death in the natural world. We also saw that Genesis does not insist that man in the garden was immortal. To the contrary, it insisted that he was not: God expelled man from the garden lest he eat the fruit of the tree of life (in which, up until the time of his expulsion, he had shown no interest) and thereby become immortal. We now need to return to the garden to see what else it says, and in particular if there is any correspondence between what it says and what we see in Olduvai Gorge, Turkana and Qafzeh.

The Genesis 1 and Genesis 2 accounts of man's origins are very different. In Genesis 1, man is the last creature to emerge. While the other creatures were 'brought forth' by the already created order (although some also needed a special creative touch),[17] man is not said to have been 'brought forth'. He is said to have been 'created', and to make the point this is repeated. Not only is he created, he is created in the image of his creator: 'So God created humankind in his image, in the image of God he created them.'[18]

The Creation of Adam: *Michelangelo*.

Being made in the image of God might have led man to expect some special endorsement from God. While God does bless man,[19] there is nothing unique about such a blessing: he has earlier blessed the water animals and the birds[20] (although not the terrestrial animals or the plants). Significantly, God withholds the endorsement that he has given to everything else that he has made (apart from the sky) – he does not say that man is 'good'.

Why not? At this stage man has not been disobedient. He is apparently morally pristine. One would not withhold the label 'good' from somebody just because you knew that they would transgress in the future.[21] Quite the opposite, in fact. If you wanted to emphasise (as the Bible may want to do) the magnitude of someone's fall from grace, it is important to emphasise that they were in grace to start with. But 'good' in Genesis cannot mean only ethically good. It is nonsensical to talk about the morality of the light, for instance.[22] The sense must be something along the lines of 'fit for purpose'. Does the primordial man, in these terms, deserve the label? No, says Leon Kass, very convincingly:

> A moment's reflection shows that man as he comes into the world is not yet good. Precisely because he is the free being, he is also the incomplete or indeterminate being; what he becomes depends always (in part) on what he freely will choose to be. Let me put it more pointedly: precisely in the sense that man is in the image of God, man is not good – not determinate, finished, complete or perfect. It remains to be seen whether man will become good, whether he will be able to complete himself (or to be completed).[23]

His purpose (the task in which his 'goodness' or otherwise will be demonstrated) is to 'be fruitful'[24] (not necessarily in just a biological way), to reproduce,[25] to fill and subdue the earth,[26] and (a gentler picture) to 'till and keep' at least the garden, if not the earth.[27]

Man gets a curiously mixed set of marks for his performance in these tasks. He gets top marks for filling the earth (he has been disastrously successful in this, and needs to stop urgently). He has similarly tilled the world far too aggressively, and ought to divert his agricultural attention from the Amazonian rainforests to the Sahara. 'Keeping' the earth implies a tender, selfless stewardship: man has failed dismally. 'Fruitful'? Well, it depends what fruit you are looking for. Mixed marks, I would say. There has been general anaesthesia, but also an increased need to use it. There has been Mother Teresa, but there have also been the slums of Calcutta. There has been Leonardo, but also the Borgias. Heroism, love and self-sacrifice have been jostled by cowardice, hate and selfishness. There has been plenty of religious ecstasy, quiet meditation and communion with the divine, but arguably a lot more humbug, hard-hearted legalism, ruthless suppression of the truth and abomination in the name of religion.

Where man has failed most disastrously is in his role as subduer. He went over very quickly to the other side, becoming one of the revolutionaries who needed to be subdued.

Genesis 1, however, ends with man standing proudly on the pinnacle of a teeming creation: the brave, free man with something of the look of the creator about him, holding the hopes of the world in his hands. It was a bold bit of delegation by God, and it was soon to go wrong.

As Genesis 2 opens, man, made out of dust before any other living thing, surveys a desert. There are no plants; there are no animals; there is no water.[28] In a small part of this wilderness God plants a garden. We are not told if there were living things outside it, or whether this was an isolated capsule of green in a hostile wasteland. We have seen already that two special trees are planted there, the tree of life and the tree of the knowledge of good and bad. Man is told that he must not eat the fruit of the tree of the knowledge of good and bad; he is given no such prohibition in relation to the tree of life. The forbidden tree of knowledge is presumably there so that man's free will can be real. Good choices are impossible if bad choices are impossible. A garden without the tree of knowledge (and therefore without the chance of catastrophe) would be a garden in which only automata could live. And you cannot have proper relationships with robots. We know, then, that this primitive man was morally awake.[29]

Most modern men, told about a tree whose fruit gave immortality, would race immediately to the tree and eat. But this man does not. He evidently has no fear of death. He does not think about his own death, as we think of ours, or as the first behaviourally modern *Homo sapiens* does. If he had any kin to bury, he would have buried them only to keep the hyenas away, and he would have wasted no flowers, let alone any valuable axe heads or bone beads, to ease the journey into the afterlife.

The first words spoken by God to the fledgling man in Genesis 2 are bounteous words: 'You may freely eat of every tree of the garden.'[30] The default rule is thus, 'It's allowed.' And the whole rule is, 'It's allowed unless it's not.' It is very permissive – outrageously permissive by the standards of many competing Mesopotamian ordinances. It is declaring that man has free will. The delegation is real. Man's choices, with one limited but very important caveat, get the divine imprimatur. The caveat follows: 'but of the tree of the knowledge of good and evil you shall not eat, for in the day that you eat of it you shall die'.[31]

Why is this prohibition thought to be necessary, when a similar prohibition in relation to the tree of life is not? Presumably because even this primordial man, whose consciousness is so embryonic that he does not acknowledge his own mortality or fear his own death, still has in him, by reason of the free will he has been bequeathed, a tendency that will nudge him towards the tree of knowledge.

The tree is a natural thing. In many ways it is an ordinary tree. It has roots, a trunk, leaves and fruit. God himself has caused it to spring from the earth. And yet it is a threat. Is this not strange? Kass suggests, and I agree, that we are being warned against presumption – against the assumption that we ourselves can learn from nature the lessons about God, ourselves and the world that we need to learn. Autonomy is dangerous: proper obedience is what we are designed for.

> Putting together the generic characteristics of 'tree' with this particular tree's name suggests that the tree of knowledge of good and bad stands for some autonomous knowledge of how to live, derived by human beings from their own experience of the visible world and rooted in their own surroundings (nature, trees in the garden). Once the potential for human freedom and choice emerges, human beings live by their own lights, learning solely from their own experience. It is precisely this natural and uninstructed human way that the Bible warns us against by having God attempt to prevent man from attaining, or even pursuing, that freedom and its correlative, autonomous knowledge ... the story means to make clear to the reader that human freedom – or, what is the same thing, human reason – is itself deeply questionable, and the likely source of all our unhappiness.[32]

The primordial man did not go around with his eyes shut. He saw the seasons pass, the storks migrating, the storms gathering over the Mediterranean and the Indian Ocean, the death of his fellows and the way that flesh turns to grass. He felt the strength of his own arm and the stirrings of an understanding of cause and effect. He learned. As he got older as a species and as an individual, he may have started to think that his knowledge amounted to real understanding. 'No it doesn't,' says this passage, 'and that delusion is deadly.'

The sanction for disobedience is interesting: 'in the day that you eat of [the forbidden tree] you shall die'. It is hardly much of a threat to a being that has no conception of death or fear of it. And when the couple do eat the fruit, they do not physically die that day. Despite being expelled from the garden, they live immensely long, apparently productive family lives. Is God lying?

We must assume that the compilers of Genesis were very well aware of the possibility of this allegation, and did not think that he was. If he was not lying, he must have been telling the truth. And if he was telling the truth, the humans did indeed die in the threatened sense when they bit into the fruit. We return shortly to wonder just what sense that was.

Up to this point, man is alone in the world. 'This', says God, 'is not good.'[33] The economy of the text is infuriating and tantalising. In what sense is it not good? Not good for the man? Not good for God? Not good for the world of which man is a steward? Not good right at that moment? Or not good given what will happen in the future? Does God's terse observation follow directly from what he has just said about the tree? Does man's physical aloneness generate dangerous self-reliance? Certainly our friends, our wives and our children are important deflators of our absurd self-importance.[34]

Whatever God means by this, he acts immediately. But he does not give the ultimate solution immediately. 'I will make him a helper as his partner,'[35] God says, but then, instead of producing a wife, forms all the living creatures out of the ground.[36] What is going on?

Were the animals the intended partners and helpers, subsequently tested and found wanting? Is the woman the shabby second-best option, reluctantly formed by God because the man is too fussy or insufficiently compliant with God's primary plan of animal partnership? It seems unlikely. '*A* helper' and '*a* partner' implies one: the seething multitude of earth's fauna is not easily described that way. And while animals can and do help, partnership implies something like equality. A shepherd and his dog, however close the bond, are not true partners. Cats, however sentimental we may get about them, are not adequate substitutes for human beings. God, too, was aiming to populate the world with humans; one man and his dog were not going to achieve that.

So why delay in producing the woman? It is no mere literary device. If the compiler of the second creation simply had to squeeze the animals into existence somehow, it would have been far less clumsy to do it at the time that the Edenic trees were planted.

Perhaps the animals were created when they were to give man a sort of apprenticeship in relationship, to let him flex his social and emotional muscles so that when the proper object of his relationship came along he would be able to hold and keep her properly.[37] It may be important, too, that man discovers and acknowledges his own need, that he recognises the inadequacy of his own and animal company. Thus Genesis says, after the man has seen (and perhaps assessed for helper and partnership potential) all the animals, 'but for the man there was not found a helper as his partner'.[38] The picture is of man looking hopefully but increasingly despairingly at each new animal that is produced, saying of each, 'It is splendid and beautiful, but it won't do.' It is another blow to man's incipient illusion of self-sufficiency. By naming the animals he has in some sense made them his; he has played some part in their creation. But 'his' animals will not do. If he is to have the only thing that can give him fulfilment and can make him fruitful, God will have to do it specially. To hammer the point home – to emphasise that man cannot be fulfilled or fruitful in his own wisdom or strength – the woman who can fulfil and can fruit is created while the man is fast asleep.[39] All bases for boasting are being systematically cut from under the man's feet.

The animals do not only provide a social and emotional gymnasium. They also give strenuous lessons in some God-like faculties which man, as image-bearer, needs to be able to use.

The Creation of Eve. Byzantine mosaic, Monreale Cathedral, Sicily.

When confronted by the animals, man speaks for the very first time in the second creation story (God has been doing a lot of speaking); man also divides, separates and categorises (which is a fair description of much of God's creative activity in the first creation story): '[God] brought [all the living creatures] to the man to see what he would call them; and whatever the man called each living creature, that was its name. The man gave names to all cattle, and to the birds of the air, and to every animal of the field . . .'[40]

Speaking, naming, cataloguing: these are all classic Upper Palaeolithic activities – but they may be very early Upper Palaeolithic activities. Man is declared to be quintessentially a social animal (it is not good for him to be alone), and a co-operative one (he needs a helper and partner). The history of humans is the history of increasingly sophisticated community.

Tilling the ground and the domestication of cattle come later in the archaeological sequence, but since we have earlier established that the compilers do not even purport to be writing strict history, we need not and should not discard the story because of some barn-door anachronisms.

Up until the creation of woman, man has apparently spoken only to name the animals. Presumably he was gruntingly laconic when he was handing out their identities. We have not heard him speak. The first time we do, we hear the first poem:

> This at last is bone of my bones
>   and flesh of my flesh;
> this one shall be called Woman,
>   for out of Man this one was taken.[41]

This is a far cry from the prosaic taxonomy of the animal-naming. Much can be said about it, but two points spring out. First, it is gloriously, unnecessarily elaborate. It is the speech of a philosopher, the stuff of bard-speak around a fire. It is from a culture that thinks there is more to man than food and sex, that adorns bodies with beads and potentially adorns ideas with adjective and metaphor. And second, it is the speech of a man replete with self-consciousness. It is reflective, and part of the reflection described is of the man's own image. He knows who and what he is, and that he is distinct from the other human who now exists. He acknowledges that she is the end of one longing, although he will find that she is not the end of all longing.

There are, however, distinct limits to the man's self-consciousness and his culture. He is not a fully realised human being. He cannot hover over himself and describe himself with dispassion. He is not the sort of being who is likely to possess many orders of theory of mind. Although he has the aesthetic impulses which will later cause him to clothe himself in finery, he is not there yet. He is naked, and it does not bother him.[42]

No sooner do language and reason sprout up than their limitations are savagely and catastrophically exposed. The snake (a natural animal, as we have seen, but the tool of some ancient bentness) uses language to corrupt. The naturalness and the dangerous craftiness of the snake are both emphasised ('now the serpent was more crafty than any other wild animal that the LORD God had made'[43]). It is yet another cautionary parable about the danger of coming to one's own conclusions about ultimate truths with the aid only of one's reason and one's observations of the natural world. Language, and its handmaiden reason, can be twisted. By themselves they cannot contain the truth. Revelation is needed too: God is needed too.

Look at how language, reason and human memory fail.

The snake said to the woman, 'Did God say, "You shall not eat from any tree in the garden?"'[44]

The correct answer was simply, 'No.' The snake is trying to make God seem a lot less generous than he actually is.

If you choose to give anything other than the simple, straightforward answer, you often get hopelessly tangled. 'The woman said to the serpent, "We may eat of the fruit of the trees in the garden; but God said, 'You shall not eat of the fruit of the tree that is in the middle of the garden, nor shall you touch it, or you shall die.'"'[45]

The woman got it wrong. The tree that is *unambiguously* in the middle of the garden was the tree of life, not the tree of the knowledge of good and evil. 'Out of the ground the LORD God made to grow every tree that is pleasant to the sight and good for food, the tree of life also in the midst of the garden, and the tree of the knowledge of good and evil.'[46] There was no prohibition at all in relation to the tree of life. And nothing at all was said about touching either tree: the woman has made that up. In the business of articulating her understanding of God's injunctions, she has made them more onerous and restrictive than they actually were. It has been the same throughout the history of religion. Not only does she add something of her own, she also misses something out. The original warning was, 'in the day that you eat of it you shall die'.[47] She renders it as simply 'you shall die'. Adding and subtracting both have their dangers.

The serpent's response is a mixture of truth and falsehood. The natural world and human reason combined do not get everything wrong. On the contrary, much of what they will jointly conclude is correct. But forget or misrepresent what God has said – what revelation has contributed – and the outcome is unlikely to be happy. 'The serpent said to the woman, "You will not die [*wrong*]; for God knows that when you eat of it your eyes will be opened [*correct*], and you will be like God, knowing good and evil [*correct*]."'[48]

The woman, prompted by her animal appetite ('the tree was good for food'), her aesthetic sensibility ('it was a delight to the eyes') and her ambitious, presumptuous desire to understand the world from a perspective that was not designed to be hers ('the tree was to be desired to make one wise'), takes the fruit, eats it, and gives it to the man.[49]

The consequences are immediate and curious: 'Then the eyes of both were opened, and they knew that they were naked; and they sewed fig leaves together and made loincloths for themselves.'[50]

They suddenly see themselves and one another fully for the first time. The embryonic consciousness inherent in man's delighted welcome to the woman has abruptly matured and been forced out into the world. They can now describe themselves to themselves and to each other. The old unconscious togetherness has evaporated. The two previously naked bodies are now separated by things of their own making. With the consciousness of self comes the consciousness of responsibility and, simultaneously, a contemptible tendency to try to shift it to others. Very young children do not blame others for their faults, it is something they grow into. That is how it was with the man and the woman. The man blames the woman, and God himself for providing the woman;[51] the woman blames the snake.[52] And they use their reason and their language to do so. When a simple 'yes' or 'no' is demanded, they seem incapable of giving it. 'Have you eaten from the tree of which I commanded you not to eat?' God asks the man.[53] The right answer is, 'Yes.' The answer the man actually gives is, 'The woman whom you gave to be with me, she gave me fruit from the tree, and I ate.'[54] Language has not fallen with the bitten fruit; it is in the very nature of language and reason to be inadequate.

We have looked already at the nature of the sentence that the humans received.[55] They are both expelled from the garden. The ground is cursed – but that curse seems only to affect the man, who will have to work hard.[56] The ground itself will hardly be bothered by it. The woman, who would apparently have had pain in childbirth anyway, will now have more of such pain.[57]

This is the famous fall of man – but was it a fall at all? Genesis is perfectly clear: the effects of the illegitimate fruit-eating *supplement* man. They do not diminish him. Eyes that were once shut are now open.[58] He sees things that were invisible to him before. 'Then the LORD God said, "See, the man has become like one of us, knowing good and evil."'[59] However you look at it, for a man fashioned from the dust, becoming like God is a rise. If this is a fall, it is a fall *up*.[60] It is common to hear Christians say that the fall has defaced the image of God in us. That may be true in a sense, but it is diametrically opposite to what Genesis says. The post-fall Adam looked *more* like God than the pre-fall Adam. The image of God in Adam was *enhanced*. That was precisely the problem.

That is not to say it was not catastrophic. It was. But what exactly is the nature of the catastrophe? God threatened that something in humans would die on the day that the fruit was tasted. But Adam is said to have lived to the age of 930,[61] and Eve, apparently, for several centuries at least.[62] Did anything die, and if so what? Man plainly did not lose that day an immortality that he already had. He had not eaten the apple of the tree of life: it had never occurred to him to eat it. He may have lost the chance to remain in the garden and one day, with a consciousness slowly evolved under the careful eye of God, be fit and proper to eat it. Perhaps that was God's hope; why else would the tree of life have been planted? But physical immortality was not the thing that died that day.

What died that day was innocence. It is always the casualty of growing self-consciousness. When children grow up and become 'sophisticated', they put on clothes and airs and do not have anything like as much fun as they did. Kass notes, of the Adam and Eve story, that 'like every truly great story, it seeks to show us not what happened (once), but what always happens, what is always the case'.[63] With sophistication came fears. Man had not touched the tree of life because it never occurred to him that he might die and that it would be a good thing to avoid that death. Now, disastrously equipped with knowledge that he was never intended to have (or at least not intended to have just yet), he could look at himself and imagine his ending. The self that had reared up could not bear the thought of its own annihilation. If man had stayed in the garden he would, like most of us, have raced for the tree. That was the reason for his expulsion: 'Then the LORD God said, "See, the man has become like one of us, knowing good and evil; and now he might reach out his hand and take also from the tree of life, and eat, and live for ever" – therefore the LORD God sent him forth from the garden of Eden.'[64]

Richard Dawkins is a better theologian than some Christians say. He has understood Christianity better than many Christians. He says that Christianity seeks to abort the growth of sophistication, and he thunders against the culture of dependence engendered by Christianity. 'Grow up,' he sneers, in what he thinks is an expression of the Renaissance spirit, but is actually a caricature of it. But 'growing up', in the sense in which he means it, is a disaster. It does not even bring happiness, let alone security. Only a fool would exchange the unselfconscious joy of a naked three-year-old for the angst of an expensively besuited fifty-year-old stockbroker. 'Unless you are born again,' said Jesus, 'you cannot see the kingdom.'[65] 'Unless you change and become like children, you will never enter the kingdom of heaven.'[66] It is the meek who inherit the earth.[67] He thanked God 'because you have hidden these things from the wise and the intelligent and have revealed them to infants'.[68]

Of the child and the stockbroker, who really knows the value of stuff? Even the *knowledge* worth having is the child's. The broker had it and lost it. The monstrous lie in the Eden story is that by reaching out and clutching the forbidden knowledge you gain more knowledge than you lose. To trade the garden for less knowledge than you gain is not very intelligent business. The broker should know better. A child has not only joy, but an intuitive wisdom that lets him skip to the conclusions to which, if he can get there at all, the sophisticate can only crawl. A child can intuit the general theory of relativity. His problem is with articulating his intuition, but who cares about that? And remember that as he accumulates years, he *unlearns* his convictions about the existence and benevolence of God.[69]

The new consciousness produced the sort of 'success' that the stockbroker would recognise. Consciousness generates symbolic thought, and symbolic thought lets you triumph over your adversaries – over neighbours (giving you power and territory), over animals (giving you good food and clothes), over your physical environment (giving you comfort). And success breeds success; consciousness breeds consciousness. Big brains (although they increase woman's pain in childbirth, as God promised) let you kill animals (which fuel your big brain better than plants do). Big brains let you be more effectively sociable and co-operative. If you are a vampire bat, you can remember with whom you shared blood; if you are a man, you can establish trade lines and run derivatives markets. Big brains breed the leisure and the comfort in which to use your symbol-manipulating powers all the more effectively. You can scheme; you can build and test in your head better shelters, better spears, better words, better computers and bigger empires, all of which, in turn, will demand still greater things of you. Since the first traces of consciousness and symbolism appear in the fossil record, human history has been characterised by this great, scrambling positive feedback.

Immediately after the expulsion from the garden, the Bible begins to tell this story. It is so obvious that we are in danger of missing it. *The direct and immediate consequence of the 'fall' is civilisation as we know it.* There is the age-old struggle between the desert and the sown – the Bedouin and the Agriculturalist – told in the story of Cain and Abel.[70] God, unsurprisingly after what we have seen so far of his preferences and intentions for man, is steadfastly on the side of the Bedouin, here and throughout the Bible. Until the very end of the Bible, God dislikes cities and everything that goes along with them. They are unhappy places, causing trouble for God and their inhabitants. Yet the disobedient humans are drawn fatally to them. Cain, whose sentence is to be a wanderer and a fugitive, ignores his sentence and settles down two verses later, founding a dynasty. Our cities are built on layer upon layer of presumption. We see culture: Jubal was 'the ancestor of all those who play the lyre and pipe'.[71] We see industry: 'Tubal-cain . . . made all kinds of bronze and iron tools.'[72] There is the occasional anachronism, but the basic story can be read in the archaeology and anthropology textbooks and in the soil. Whether or not the individuals mentioned are historical, their stories are accurately paradigmatic.

If you want to look for an historical Adam and Eve, I suggest that you look among those anatomically modern but behaviourally naive *Homo sapiens*. Just like the biblical Adam and Eve, they had an abrupt change. Something non-anatomical but profound happened to them which transmuted dramatically the whole way that they looked at themselves, at one another and at the world; which gave them self-consciousness, a fear of death and a taste for bangles; which catapulted their society and the world into a catastrophic sophistication. All this was a consequence of the new, far-reaching ability to ask, 'What if?' – which was precisely the question that God, for some reason, did not want man to ask. Any historian can appreciate God's concern. All the unpleasant parts in the history of humanity are to do with the asking and the devastating answering of 'What if?' type questions.

We have no idea what the trigger was.[73] For all we know, it could have been the biting of a forbidden apple.

It would be tidier to leave the matter there, but we cannot do that. It is not just wars, obscenities and neuroses that result from 'What if?' type questions. It is Mozart, general anaesthesia, Shakespeare, penicillin and the rule of law. It is legitimate, fulfilling aspiration as well as diabolical presumption. In fact, it is all human history, not just the shameful bits. Did God really want us to miss out on the intense pleasures of imagination and speculation? Was the cost of culture really too high? Is his vision for humans really Rousseau's noble savage?

The only exegetically honest answer that tallies with the archaeological record is that he did indeed want us to miss out. The cost of culture was a cost that he thought was too high.

Our natural reaction to this is that it is ridiculous; that God, if he wants to keep us as neonates, cannot be worth respecting; that it is absurdly defensive of him to be afraid of us growing up. No decent human parent, however much they value innocence, spontaneity and unfettered intuition in their child, would chronologically fossilise their toddler.

Perhaps we think this because one of the major consequences of the fall is that we can no longer see the majestic possibilities and the stupendous charisma of innocence. We see innocence as merely the absence of transgression, and think that it is dull. 'Virgin' has become a term of abuse.

Just occasionally, maybe, we bump for a moment into proper, unmistakable holiness – in a person, in an idea, in a picture. And for a second, before the fallen sophisticate in us begins to scoff, an exhilarating shock runs through us – a shock that takes its charge from a deeply implanted subliminal memory of what we once were, a shameful realisation of what we are, and a thrilling hope of what we might be. The very, very last thing we would say about that encounter is that it was boring.

'I do not doubt', wrote C.S. Lewis, 'that if the Paradisal man could now appear among us, we should regard him as an utter savage, a creature to be exploited or, at best, patronised. Only one or two, and those the holiest among us, would glance a second time at the naked, shaggy-bearded, slow-spoken creature: but they, after a few minutes, would fall at his feet.'[74]

The Neanderthals were not the greatest intuiters ever. That title must go to the pre-symbolic *Homo sapiens* who did not re-create the world in the image of themselves and their thoughts, but rather engaged with it, in all its immediacy and undiluted otherness, with an intensity of which we grey adults can only dream. They were soaked in the world. Our symbols act as a skin which prevents the world getting close. We listen enraptured to the Bach *B Minor Mass*, and say that it is one of the things about our highly cognate culture that must have been given to us by God. Hence the theological leap, away from those terribly difficult words in Genesis, to the wrong conclusion that whatever the fall did, Bach could not have been a *consequence* of it. But what Bach does is to remind us, very faintly, very imperfectly, of a relationship with the world – with God – that we once had. Bach is a hint. The men in the garden had the real thing. We have gained nothing by having Bach (although, of course, it is far better to have him now than not have him at all). He tells us about flowers; the men in the garden lay in beds of them. He describes, in the terse words of wine-tasting notes, the flavour of an almost-forgotten drink; the men in the garden drank it neat, and by the bucketful. We read books about God, he hovers in the room, often barely distinguishable from our imagination, and sometimes he bursts in; they breathed him. If Bach played in the garden, would he harmonise symphonically with its sounds, or would he jar? I am not sure, but I suspect the worst.

I do not know where these thoughts lead. The obvious suggestions are that they point to the East, or into the Sacred Feminine. I reject both suggestions, for reasons that have no place in this book.

We cannot stop yet. There is one further strand.

In a secure room in the British Library, within earshot of the thundering chaos of the Euston Road, lies a very short, very dog-eared fifteenth-century manuscript. It is a song, thought to be the work of a wandering minstrel. It tells the story of the garden, but it also comments on the story in a very strange way.

> Adam lay ybounden,
> Bounden in a bond;
> Four thousand winter,
> Thought he not too long.
> And all was for an apple,

An apple that he took.
As clerkes finden,
Written in their book.
Ne had the apple taken been,
The apple taken been,
Ne had never our ladie,
Abeen heav'ne queen.
Blessed be the time
That apple taken was,
Therefore we moun singen.
Deo gracias!

'*Blessed* be the time' that the apple was taken? But why? Was it not the time of the greatest catastrophe the cosmos has ever seen?

It was blessed, says the song, because if the apple had not been taken, Mary would never have been Queen of Heaven. It is code: if the apple had not been taken, it is saying, the incarnation would never have happened. If the theological logic of the song is right, the *solution* to the problem of the fall goes hugely beyond a repair: we are left so much better off that we ought to give extravagant thanks for the defect that brought the workman in. It is as if we break a tap, and the plumber not only fixes the tap but rebuilds the whole house as a palace and paints it with the skill of a Michelangelo.

We were designed for an oasis, but we end up, if Revelation is right, in a city. It seems as if God has abandoned his preference for nomads and come to terms with civilisation. The possibilities for community, co-operation and altruism there are far greater than in the goatskin tent by the water-hole. Something has been lost on the journey there, but it has been restored, as Job found, many times over. It is not mere restoration: the cosmos has been transformed to allow a fulfilment of which Adam could never have dreamed.

CHAPTER 10

Living with God and Darwin

> If [biologists] are honest, they may feel a sense of unease about
> the fluidity and grace of adaptation. It has an almost uncanny
> sense of precision and balance, which humans achieve only rarely
> in technology or art ... The complexity and beauty of 'Life's
> Solution' can never cease to astound. None of it presupposes,
> let alone proves, the existence of God, but all is congruent.
>
> (Simon Conway Morris, *Life's Solution*)[1]

Richard Dawkins relates the story of Kurt Wise, a brilliant and
promising American geologist, who studied under Stephen Jay
Gould at Harvard. He had been brought up as a Young Earth
creationist. He struggled for years to reconcile the two different
worlds, and one day the struggle came to a head. Taking a pair
of scissors, he went through his Bible, cutting out every verse
that he saw as inconsistent with his religious world view. There
was not much left.

> Try as I might, and even with the benefit of intact margins
> throughout the pages of Scripture, I found it impossible to pick
> up the Bible without it being rent in two. I had to make a deci-
> sion between evolution and Scripture. Either the Scripture was
> true and evolution was wrong or evolution was true and I must
> toss out the Bible ... It was there that night that I accepted
> the Word of God and rejected all that would ever counter it,
> including evolution. With that, in great sorrow, I tossed into
> the fire all my dreams and hopes in science ... if all the evidence

in the universe turns against creationism, I would be the first to admit it, but I would still be a creationist because that is what the Word of God seems to indicate. Here I must stand.[2]

Dawkins finds that a tragic story, and surely it is. Dawkins also praises Wise's honesty, and surely that is right too. Either creationism or science has to be slung on the fire: there is no way to pretend that they are the same.

But the story is mainly tragic because it is so unnecessary. Wise's brain is needed in geology, and there is absolutely no reason why he should not have stayed there and flourished.

Dawkins loves the story because it expresses beautifully his own world view – that you have to choose between science and Christianity. He and Kurt Wise are intellectual bedfellows. Their mistakes are identical. They both think that all the answers to all the questions in the universe are to be found within a single text. For Wise, the text is the Bible (probably the King James Version, I should think). For Dawkins, it is an undiluted Darwinian adaptationism. And neither has read his own text properly, let alone the text of the other. Almost nobody in evolutionary biology believes that things are as simple as Dawkins thinks they are. Darwin certainly did not – he said so expressly. And the whole history of the evolution of evolution has been to insert fascinating, intriguing caveats into Darwin's basic theory. They are all wasted on Dawkins and Dennett, who, with the bright staring eyes of the true fanatic, continue to preach the pure Darwinian gospel long after everyone else has realised that things are not so straightforward.

That is exactly what Kurt Wise does. There are no serious biblical scholars anywhere in the world who believe what he does. You do not have to read very deeply into the Bible to realise that the compilers of the Bible themselves intended expressly to repudiate his view. In the first two chapters of

Genesis, for goodness' sake, there are two wholly mutually exclusive accounts of the creation of the world.

Real, full-blooded Darwinism, marked and scarred where it has engaged properly with the world, is a hugely more compelling creed than the one peddled in the paperbacks and accepted uncritically by scientifically unlettered people who want some sort of scientific excuse to rubbish religion. Real, full-blooded Christianity, acknowledging the absurdity of anaemic literalism, confronting the challenges of the Bible (a very difficult, cryptic, challenging document) and the world (a very difficult, cryptic, challenging place), is a hugely more compelling creed than the one peddled in the fundamentalist ghettos by the fearful and the fearfully dogmatic.

Two strong, self-critical doctrines like proper Darwinism and proper Christianity have a lot to say to each other.

Darwinism provides an immensely powerful explanation for much of what has happened and is happening in the natural world. It is not just a potential explanation: there is no doubt at all that it has shaped a lot of what we see whenever we go outdoors. Although natural selection has not been shown to produce speciation (macro-evolution), it has been shown to effect micro-evolution, and to effect it, in some circumstances, really quite fast. Although speciation remains something of a biological black box, the Darwinist inference (that if you have enough micro-evolution for long enough, you will get macro-evolution) seems sensible.

And yet, speak gently to any orthodox Darwinian, and he will admit that the power and therefore the speed of natural selection are notoriously difficult to assess. Occasionally it can be done easily – for instance when you look at bacterial resistance to antibiotics. But there are very few natural examples remotely analogous to that. If you cannot measure the power and speed of natural selection, you cannot begin to say that natural selection was powerful enough to produce the change that actually occurred in the relevant time period. Still less can you begin to say that other forces could not have had a hand in effecting that change. Modern theistic evolutionists have been too ready to agree that natural selection is the only candidate.[3] The concession is not only biologically unnecessary, but requires some dangerous downplaying of the unavoidable problem of pain, death and waste.

The vantage point from which we view the natural world determines crucially what we see. Most biologists, marinated since their intellectual birth in Darwinism, tend to see organismal self-interest as the engine of change wherever they look.

There is in the world, and has been since very early in the history of life, a great deal of *association*. The first organisms were single celled, but they soon clustered together to form first loose and then tighter conglomerations. Eventually the conglomerations became multicellular organisms, and as soon as we see multicellular organisms we see conglomerations of increasing complexity between those multicellular organisms. It has become trite to observe that the history of evolution is the history of increasing complexity. But that can be put rather differently. It can be said that the history of evolution is the history of increasing sociation and community. Not only is community an example of complexity, but the more complex you are, the more sociable, co-operative and apparently altruistic you can be. If the only force pushing the biological world onwards is Darwinian natural selection, then natural selection is pushing it constantly in a direction that favours community, co-operation and altruism.

Co-operation and altruism cannot be seen in the fossil record[4]; they are things that one sees only in live organisms. But they are everywhere that one looks in the living world. Orthodox Darwinism says that co-operation and 'altruism' are actually just examples of selfishness at work, and has devised some ingenious theories to explain this. But those theories have problems, and they have been examined in this book. One of the most obvious and fundamental problems is how a wholly self-centred process (natural selection), that normally sees and eliminates very effectively any self-effacing behaviour, could have allowed altruism to seed in the first place. Once it is seeded, it is easy enough to see that it might confer an advantage that will be favoured by natural selection.

There is no need for the intellectual gymnastics of the Darwinists who feel the need to explain all community and apparent altruism as selfishness. Put down the Darwinist lens just for a moment (and remember that it cannot be proved that it is the only one through which one gets a worthwhile view). Look again at the immensely long history of life. Consider the possibility that something might be exactly what it seems to be. It looks as if, consistently, another force has been at work moulding the shape of the biological world – the force of community, of altruism, of selflessness. Sometimes this force might have been the tool of natural selection – there is no problem at all with that. Sometimes it might have been a self-energising force.

If this is right, or if it may be right, the Darwinist biologist on the tangled bank need not think that it is embarrassingly un-Darwinian to have given his guide the paracetamol. The way will be open for him to rejoice again, as he did as a boy, in the beauty of the world, in the iridescence of the beetles. He need not think that all the beauty is purely the product of death, pain, selfishness and struggle. The poems his mother loved need not be victims of a grey reductionism. He might even go back to the tangled book and find there, buried in some old, wise words, a reason why he threw flowers into his mother's grave and gave his beetles individual names.

Select Bibliography

This book ranges over many fields. The literature in each of those fields is immense. This bibliography is a very small selection of some of the more accessible books. It is intended as a starting point for anyone wanting to take things further.

Alexander, Denis, *Creation or Evolution: Do We Have to Choose?* (Oxford: Lion Hudson, 2008).

Aunger, Robert (ed.), *Darwinizing Culture: The Status of Memetics as a Science* (Oxford: Oxford University Press, 2000).

Barrett, Justin, *Why Would Anyone Believe in God?* (Walnut Creek, California/Oxford: Altamira Press, 2004).

Berry, Andrew, *Infinite Tropics: An Alfred Russel Wallace Anthology* (New York: Verso, 2002).

Berry, Robert (Sam), *God and the Biologist: Faith at the Frontiers of Science* (Leicester: Apollos, 1996).

Berry, Robert (Sam), *God's Book of Works: The Nature and Theology of Nature: Glasgow Gifford Lectures* (London and New York: T & T Clark/Continuum, 2003).

Blackmore, Susan, *The Meme Machine* (Oxford: Oxford University Press, 1999).

Canfield, John, *Becoming Human: The Development of Language, Self, and Self-consciousness* (Basingstoke: Palgrave Macmillan, 2007).

Clayton, Philip, and Jeffrey Schloss, *Evolution and Ethics: Human Morality in Biological and Religious Perspective* (Grand Rapids, Michigan: Eerdmans, 2004).

Collins, Francis, *The Language of God: A Scientist Presents Evidence for Belief* (New York and London: Free Press, 2006).

Conway Morris, Simon, *The Crucible of Creation: The Burgess Shale and the Rise of Animals* (Oxford: Oxford University Press, 1998).

Conway Morris, Simon, *Life's Solution: Inevitable Humans in a Lonely Universe* (Cambridge: Cambridge University Press, 2003).

Conway Morris, Simon (ed.), *The Deep Structure of Biology: Is Convergence Sufficiently Ubiquitous to Give a Directional Signal?* (West Conshohocken: Templeton Foundation, 2008).

Darwin, Charles, *The Origin of Species by Means of Natural Selection, or the Preservation of Favoured Races in the Struggle for Life* (London: John Murray, 1859).

Dawkins, Richard, *The Selfish Gene* (Oxford: Oxford University Press, 1976).

Dawkins, Richard, *The Blind Watchmaker* (New York: Norton, 1987).

Dawkins, Richard, *Climbing Mount Improbable* (London: Viking, 1996).

Dawkins, Richard, *A Devil's Chaplain: Selected Essays* (London: Weidenfeld and Nicolson, 2003).

Dawkins, Richard, *The Ancestor's Tale: A Pilgrimage to the Dawn of Life* (London: Weidenfeld and Nicolson, 2004).

Dawkins, Richard, *The God Delusion* (London: Bantam Press, 2006).

Dennett, Daniel, *Darwin's Dangerous Idea: Evolution and the Meanings of Life* (London: Allen Lane, 1995).

Dennett, Daniel, *Breaking the Spell: Religion as a Natural Phenomenon* (London: Penguin, 2007).

Diamond, Jared, *The Third Chimpanzee: The Evolution and*

Future of the Human Animal (New York: Harper Perennial, 2006).

Drees, Willem (ed.), *Is Nature Ever Evil? Religion, Science and Value* (London: Routledge, 2003).

Dunbar, Robin, *The Human Story: A New History of Mankind's Evolution* (London: Faber and Faber, 2004).

Dunbar, Robin, and Louise Barrett (ed.), *Oxford Handbook of Evolutionary Psychology* (Oxford: Oxford University Press, 2007).

Edwards, Denis, *The God of Evolution* (Mahway, NJ: Paulist Press, 1999).

Forrest, Barbara, and Paul Gross, *Creationism's Trojan Horse: The Wedge of Intelligent Design* (Oxford: Oxford University Press, 2003).

Fowler, Thomas, and Daniel Kuebler, *The Evolution Controversy: A Survey of Competing Theories* (Grand Rapids, Michigan: Baker Academic, 2007).

Gould, Stephen Jay, *Wonderful Life: The Burgess Shale and the Nature of History* (New York: W.W. Norton, 1989).

Gould, Stephen Jay, *Eight Little Piggies* (New York: W.W. Norton, 1993).

Gould, Stephen Jay, *Rocks of Ages: Science and Religion in the Fullness of Life* (New York: Ballantine, 1999).

Haught, John, *God after Darwin: A Theology of Evolution* (Oxford and Boulder, CO: Westview Press, 2000).

Haught, John, *Deeper than Darwin: The Prospect for Religion in an Age of Evolution* (Oxford and Boulder, CO: Westview Press, 2003).

Humphrey, Nicholas, *The Mind Made Flesh: Essays from the Frontiers of Psychology and Religion* (Oxford: Oxford University Press, 2002).

Kass, Leon, *The Beginning of Wisdom: Reading Genesis* (Chicago: University of Chicago Press, 2006).

Kohn, Marek, *A Reason for Everything: Natural Selection and the English Imagination* (London: Faber and Faber, 2004).

Lewis, C.S., *The Problem of Pain* (London: Geoffrey Bles, 1940).

Linzey, Andrew, and Dorothy Yamamoto, *Animals on the Agenda: Questions about Animals for Theology and Ethics* (London: SCM, 1998).

Linzey, Andrew, *Creatures of the Same God: Explorations in Animal Theology* (Winchester: Winchester University Press, 2007).

Lloyd, Michael, *Café Theology* (London: Alpha, 2005).

Lucas, Ernest, *Can We Believe Genesis Today? The Bible and Questions of Science* (Leicester: Inter-Varsity Press, 2001).

McGrath, Alister, *Dawkins' God: Genes, Memes and the Meaning of life* (Oxford: Blackwell, 2004).

McGrath, Alister, and Joanna Collicutt McGrath, *The Dawkins Delusion: Atheist Fundamentalism and the Denial of the Divine* (London: SPCK, 2007).

Messer, Neil, *Selfish Genes and Christian Ethics: Theological and Ethical Reflections on Evolutionary Biology* (London: SCM, 2007).

Miller, Keith (ed.), *Perspectives on an Evolving Creation* (Grand Rapids, Michigan: Eerdmans, 2003).

Miller, Kenneth, *Finding Darwin's God* (New York: HarperCollins, 1999).

Newberg, Andrew, and Mark Waldman, *Born to Believe: God, Science and the Origin of Ordinary and Extraordinary Beliefs* (New York: Simon and Schuster, 2006).

Numbers, Ronald L., *The Creationists: From Scientific Creationism to Intelligent Design* (Cambridge, MA: Harvard University Press, 2006).

Pasternak, Charles (ed.), *What Makes Us Human?* (Oxford: Oneworld, 2007).

Polkinghorne, John, *Science and Creation: The Search for Understanding* (London: SPCK, 1988).

Polkinghorne, John, *Scientists as Theologians: A Comparison of the Writings of Ian Barbour, Arthur Peacocke and John Polkinghorne* (London: SPCK, 1996).

Polkinghorne, John (ed.), *The Work of Love: Creation as Kenosis* (Grand Rapids, Michigan: Eerdmans, 2001).

Polkinghorne, John, *One World: The Interaction of Science and Theology* (London: Templeton Foundation, 2007).

Richerson, Peter, *Not by Genes Alone: How Culture Transformed Human Evolution* (Chicago: University of Chicago Press, 2005).

Ridley, Mark (ed.), *Evolution* (Oxford: Oxford University Press, 2004).

Ridley, Matt, *The Origins of Virtue* (London: Viking, 1996).

Ruse, Michael, *The Evolution-Creation Struggle* (Cambridge, MA: Harvard University Press, 2005).

Scott, Eugenie, *Evolution vs Creationism* (Berkeley: University of California Press, 2004).

Southgate, Christopher, *The Groaning of Creation: God, Evolution and the Problem of Evil* (Louisville: Westminster John Knox Press, 2008).

Tattersall, Ian, *Becoming Human: Evolution and Human Uniqueness* (Oxford: Oxford University Press, 1998).

Tattersall, Ian, and Jeffrey Schwartz, *Extinct Humans* (Boulder, CO: Westview Press, 2000).

Tattersall, Ian, *The Monkey in the Mirror: Essays on the Science of What Makes Us Human* (Oxford: Oxford University Press, 2002).

Tattersall, Ian, *The World from Beginnings to 4000 BCE* (New York/Oxford: Oxford University Press, 2008).

Ward, Keith, *Religion and Creation* (Oxford: Oxford University Press, 1996).

Williams, Patricia, *Doing without Adam and Eve: Sociobiology and Original Sin* (Minneapolis: Fortress Press, 2001).

Wolpert, Lewis, *Six Impossible Things before Breakfast: The Evolutionary Origins of Belief* (London: Faber and Faber, 2006).

Wright, N.T., *Evil and the Justice of God* (Downers Grove, IL: InterVarsity Press, 2007).

Young, Matt, and Taner Edis (eds), *Why Intelligent Design Fails: A Scientific Critique of the New Creationism* (New Brunswick, NJ: Rutgers University Press, 2004).

Notes

Preface

1. See http://www.guardian.co.uk/education/2006/aug/15/higheredu-
cation.students.
2. John Haught, *God after Darwin: A theology of evolution* (Oxford
and Boulder, CO.: Westview Press, 2000), p. 2.

Chapter 1

1. Several species of bee hawk moths have adopted this strategy.
2. A reference to 'Darwin's orchids': *Epipactis* sp.
3. The creationist here is a Young Earth creationist. There are Old
Earth creationists who believe, for instance, that the biblical days
of creation represent 'ages'.
4. Gen. 1:29–30. Note, though, that the diet of men and animals
was not the same. Humans were to eat seed-yielding plants; the
other animals were to eat green plants.
5. Gen. 1:22, 28.
6. Gen. 1:26–8.
7. Gen. 2:4–7, 19.
8. Gen. 2:18–20.
9. Nobody knows how many species exist on the earth today. There
could easily be 20 million. It seems very likely that there were
hundreds of millions of species that are now extinct. There may
well have been billions.
10. Richard Dawkins puts it well: 'All who have given thought to the
matter agree that an apparatus as complex as the human eye
could not possibly come into existence through [a single chance
event]. Unfortunately the same seems to be true of at least parts

of the apparatus of cellular machinery whereby DNA replicates itself . . .' He goes on to conclude that the complexity of the most basic mechanisms required for DNA replication means that any theory that asserts that such a mechanism arose from mere chance is utterly unbelievable. See *The Blind Watchmaker* (New York: Norton, 1987), pp. 140–1.

11. Thomas Huxley (1825–95) was an English biologist. He was known as 'Darwin's Bulldog' for his articulate and energetic propounding of Darwin's theories.

12. Thomas Malthus (1766–1834), English economist and demographer. He noted that there was potential for massive, geometric increase in population, exceeding the ability of the economy to support that population. He also noted that such increases were not generally seen, because of the inhibiting effect of many factors, for instance the food supply.

13. Charles Darwin, *The Origin of Species by Means of Natural Selection, or the Preservation of Favoured Races in the Struggle for Life* (London: John Murray, 1859).

14. The synthesis was the work of many, but notably J.B.S. Haldane (1892–1964), Ronald Fisher (1890–1962) and Sewall Wright (1889–1988) in the 1920s and 30s.

15. The cause of the Cretaceous-Tertiary boundary event is still contentious. The asteroid theory probably leads the field.

16. To be fair to Richard Dawkins, who is criticized by implication here, he has said that 'Any orthodox Darwinian would be entirely happy with major extinctions being largely a matter of luck'; in *A Devil's Chaplain: Selected Essays* (London: Weidenfeld and Nicolson, 2003), p. 240.

17. David Campbell and Keith Miller see God behind all this: 'Given his pattern of action in history, surely we can envision [God] declaring: "But you, Chordata, though you are small among the phyla of animals, out of you will come for me rulers of the earth . . ."'; in 'The "Cambrian Explosion": A Challenge to Evolutionary Theory?', in Keith B. Miller (ed.), *Perspectives on an Evolving Creation* (Grand Rapids, Michigan: Eerdmans, 2003), p. 204.

18. Pierre-Simon Laplace (1749–1827) was a French astronomer and

mathematician. He presented a copy of his great work, *Celestial Mechanics*, to Napoleon. Napoleon remarked that Laplace had made no mention of God. 'Sir,' replied Laplace, 'I had no need of that hypothesis.'

19. Stephen Jay Gould, 'Darwinian Fundamentalism', *New York Review of Books*, 1997, 44:10. Available at http://www.nybooks.com/articles/1151.

20. Darwin, *The Origin of Species*. Interestingly, in the second edition, published one month after the first, Darwin amended this conclusion to read, '... breathed *by the Creator* into ...' (emphasis mine).

21. Vladimir Nabokov, *Nabokov's Butterflies: Unpublished and Uncollected Writings*, ed. Robert Pyle and Brian Boyd (Boston, MA: Beacon Press, 2000), pp. 85–6.

Chapter 2

1. Dawkins, *A Devil's Chaplain*, p. 226.

2. Calvin noted, 'If we hold the Spirit of God to be the only source of truth, we will neither reject nor despise the truth, wherever it may reveal itself, lest we offend the Spirit of God'; in *Institutes of the Christian Religion* (1536). That means taking fossils and molecular clocks seriously.

3. *In Memoriam* (1850).

4 Or so it is said. Even this could be fiction. Controversy rages.

5. Letter, Charles Kingsley to Charles Darwin, 18 November 1859. Letter number 2534 in the Darwin correspondence. See http://www.darwinproject.ac.uk/darwin/search/query?query=deity&searchphrase=any&order=newest.

6 William Jennings Bryan (1860–1925), for instance, who attributed most modern ills to the ubiquity of belief in evolution.

7 Henry Morris, *King of Creation* (San Diego: CLP Publishing, 1980).

8. Stephen Jay Gould, *Hen's Teeth and Horses' Toes* (New York: W. W. Norton, 1983), p. 260, cited in Dawkins, *A Devil's Chaplain*, p. 233.

9. William Bermetta, Fellow of the Californian Academy of Sciences, cited in Ernest Lucas, 'God and Origins: Interpreting the Early Chapters of Genesis', Lecture at the Faraday Institute, 2007.

10. *The Origin of Species* (6th ed., 1872).

11. See Marek Kohn, *A Reason for Everything: Natural Selection and the English Imagination* (London: Faber and Faber, 2004).

12. Gould, 'Darwinian Fundamentalism'.

Chapter 3

1. Ockham's razor is the principle *Entia non sunt multiplicanda praeter necessitatem*: 'entities should not be multiplied unnecessarily'.

2. See the discussion in *The Blind Watchmaker*, chapter 3, 'Accumulating small change'.

3. Richard Dawkins, *Climbing Mount Improbable* (London: Viking, 1996).

4. And of course I hope the same tactic works for this book.

5. Ian Tattersall, *The Monkey in the Mirror: Essays on the Science of What Makes Us Human* (Oxford: Oxford University Press, 2002), pp. 50–1.

6. Per Karl Popper, et al. There are, of course, other (less general) criteria, including (importantly in this context) the ability to make predictions about things that may happen or may have happened but have not yet been observed. An example of this predictive criterion in the context of evolutionary biology is the prediction of future findings in the fossil record. We will see some examples in this book.

7. J.B.S. Haldane (1892–1964), one of the great architects of the neo-Darwinian synthesis.

8. There are other contentions, notably gravitational time dilation and alternate synchrony, both of which rely on general relativity. Neither has been published in any peer-reviewed journal or had any support from mainstream science. They are summarised well in Thomas Fowler and Daniel Kuebler, *The Evolution Controversy* (Grand Rapids, MI: Baker Academic, 2007), pp. 205–8.

9. Barry Setterfield and Trevor Norman, *The Atomic Constants, Light and Time* (privately printed), available at www.setterfield.org/report/report.html.

10. The arguments are well summarised in Lee Strobel, *The Case for a Creator* (Grand Rapids, MI: Zondervan, 2004), pp. 125–52.

11. The conversion factor is 450,000.

12. To be entirely accurate, if the Earth were infinitely old, the protons would all have decayed.

13. There is a very accessible account of the mechanism of radiometric dating, and the objections to the methodology, in Darrell Falk, *Coming to Peace with Science* (Downers Grove, IL: IVP Academic, 2004), pp. 62–73.

14. See Keith Swensen, 'Is the lava dome at Mount St Helen's really a million years old?', 1998, http://www.creationism.org/articles/swenson1.htm.

15. For a more detailed discussion of the issue, see Fowler and Kuebler, *The Evolution Controversy*, pp. 219–21.

16. These last three methods are discussed in more detail in Falk, *Coming to Peace with Science*, pp. 73–4.

17. See John Alroy, cited in Simon Conway Morris, *Life's Solution: Inevitable Humans in a Lonely Universe* (Cambridge: Cambridge University Press, 2003), p. 306. This tendency to increasing size is known as Cope's Rule, and although it is often seen, there are plenty of counter-examples of miniaturization (and indeed simplification).

18. About 90 per cent of all species living in the Permian (290 to 245 million years ago) did not survive into the succeeding Mesozoic period. There was another great extinction at the end of the Mesozoic, which famously included the dinosaurs.

19. The phenomenon of spherical aberration.

20. See the discussion in Conway Morris, *Life's Solution*, pp. 151–4.

21. There is disagreement between creationists as to when the flood came. Some put it in the upper Palaeozoic, others in the late Cenozoic.

22. These are red algae. A case could be made for community even before that. The cyanobacteria that formed the stromatolites in

Australia's Apex chert, nearly 3.5 billion years ago, formed the stromatolites precisely because they all lived together.

23. Note, for instance, the Ediacaran fossils, originally named after the beds in South Australia where they were originally found, but now represented in several sites throughout the world. Of course fossil algae, bacteria and more sophisticated unicellular eukaryotes are also found throughout the Pre-Cambrian.

24. See Campbell and Miller, 'The "Cambrian Explosion"', in Miller, *Perspectives on an Evolving Creation*, p. 196. Simon Conway Morris (personal communication, 2008) points out that this view of a post-Cambrian slowdown is an over-simplification. He notes that the post-Cambrian evolution of nervous systems and mutualism make precisely the opposite point, and contends that 'even in terms of overall diversity the succeeding Ordovician radiations are in some ways more impressive.'

25. A typical example of the traditional creationist position towards the evolution of the horse is at http://www.angelfire.com/mi/dinosaurs/horse.html. For a discussion of the creationist position towards common descent and transitional forms in general, and horse evolution in particular, see Keith Miller, 'Common Descent, Transitional Forms and the Fossil Record', in Miller, *Perspectives on an Evolving Creation*, pp. 152–81.

26. A detailed account of this is in Falk, *Coming to Peace with Science*, pp. 116–18.

27. James Brierley Smith, *Old Fourlegs: The Story of the Coelacanth* (London: Longmans and Green, 1956). For a detailed account of the search for the coelacanth, see Samantha Weinberg, *A Fish Caught in Time: The Search for the Coelacanth* (New York: HarperCollins, 2006).

28. Ernst Haeckel (1834–1919). It has been claimed by some creationists that Darwin relied on Haeckel's drawings in formulating his theory. This is wrong: *The Origin of Species* was published in 1859; Haeckel's drawings were published in 1874.

29. Darwin himself, of course, did not realise their significance until much later.

30. A good example of the difficulty appears in the discussion in

Burridge, et al., 'Geological Dates and Molecular Rates: Fish DNA Sheds Light on Time Dependency', *Molecular Biology and Evolution*, 25:4, 2008, pp. 624–33.

31. See http://evolution.berkeley.edu/evosite/evo101/IIE1cMolecularclocks.

32. This account is based on the much more detailed version in Fowler and Kuebler, *The Evolution Controversy*, pp. 103–7.

33. Carl Wieland, 'Speciation Conference brings good news for creationists', http://www.answersingenesis.org/TJ/v11/i2/speciation.asp, 1997 (original emphasis).

34. Ken Ham, 'Did God create poodles?', http://www.answersingenesis.org/creation/v25/i4/poodles.asp, 2003.

35. See E. Verheyen, et al., 'Origin of the superflock of cichlid fishes from Lake Victoria, East Africa', *Science*, 300:5617, 2003, pp. 325–9.

36. See, for instance, M.J. Genner, et al., 'Age of cichlids: New data for ancient lake fish radiation', *Molecular Biology and Evolution*, 24:1269–82, 2007; Burridge, et al., 'Geological Dates and Molecular Rates'.

37. See B.M. Rothschild, D.H. Tanke, M. Helbling II and L.D. Martin, 'Epidemologic study of tumors in dinosaurs', *Naturwissenschafte*, 90(11), 2003, pp. 495–500.

38. Dawkins, *A Devil's Chaplain*, p. 224.

39. Stephen Jay Gould, 'The Panda's Thumb', *Natural History*, 87(9), 1978, pp. 20–30.

40. Chapter 6. He continued, 'No doubt many organs exist of which we do not know the transitional grades, more especially if we look to much-isolated species, round which, according to my theory, there has been much extinction. Or again, if we look to an organ common to all the members of a large class, for in this latter case the organ must have been first formed at an extremely remote period, since which all the many members of the class have been developed; and in order to discover the early transitional grades through which the organ has passed, we should have to look to very ancient ancestral forms, long since become extinct. We should be extremely cautious in concluding that an organ could not have been formed by transitional gradations of some kind.'

41. See, for instance, Michael Behe, *Darwin's Black Box* (New York: Simon and Schuster, 1996).

42. See the section on 'Falsifiability: intelligent design', at pp. 41–3.

43. The recent work is accessibly summarised in Dan Jones, 'Engines of Evolution', *New Scientist*, 16 February 2008, pp. 40–3.

44. J.B.S. Haldane, 'A Mathematical Theory of Natural and Artificial Selection', Part 1, *Transactions of the Cambridge Philosophical Society*, 23, 1924, pp. 19–41, cited in Kohn, *A Reason for Everything*, p. 154.

45. R.A. Fisher, *The Genetical Theory of Natural Selection: A Complete Variorum Edition* (Oxford: Oxford University Press, 1999), cited in Kohn, ibid., p. 104. See too R.A. Fisher, *Evolution as a Process* (1954).

46. See Kohn, ibid., p. 105.

47. See Dawkins, *The Blind Watchmaker*, chapter 3.

48. Cited in Kohn, *A Reason for Everything*, p. 130.

Chapter 4

1. Cited by Matt Ridley, in *The Origins of Virtue* (London: Viking, 1996), p. 7. Several of the examples in this chapter are discussed in more detail there.

2. Darwin, *The Origin of Species*, chapter 6.

3. William Hamilton, 'The genetical evolution of social behaviour', I, II, *Journal of Theoretical Biology*, 7:1–52, 1964, cited in Ridley, *The Origins of Virtue*, p. 18.

4. Some of the recent trends are well summarised in Kevin Kniffen, David Wilson and Jeffrey Schloss, 'Evolutionary Research on Altruism', in Stephen Post, Byron Johnson, Michael McCullough and Jeffrey Schloss (eds), *Research on Altruism and Love: An Annotated Bibliography of Major Studies in Psychology, Sociology, Evolutionary Biology, and Theology* (West Conshohocken, PA: Templeton Foundation Press, 2002).

5. If apparent altruism has not been positively selected for, there may be other explanations. Altruism may be a side effect of something else that has been selected for, and is insufficiently damaging

to the individual to have been selected out, or it may be a manifestation of something selected for in the past but which is maladaptive in present circumstances. We return later to these ideas.

6. See E.O. Wilson, 'Kin Selection as the key to altruism: its rise and fall', *Social Research*, Spring 2005. He concludes there: 'The research on collateral kin selection was a thriving industry for three decades. Thanks to the detour given it by Trivers' correction of Hamilton's arithmetical error, kin selection theory opened a new realm of research on conflict in societies, fruitful not only in the study of social insects ... but also in parent-offspring studies ... genomic imprinting in developmental biology ... and in evolutionary psychology, the human-oriented discipline spinoff from socio-biology ... The collapse of the haplodiploid hypothesis, reducing collateral kin selection to a weak dissolutive role, gives reason to place more emphasis on the ecological forces of colony-level selection, and hence the complex ergonomic devices of caste and communication that adapt colonies to those forces. All of these developments in sociobiology are in full progress, and surprises no doubt lie ahead. The interpretation I have presented here may itself in time be swept aside. New evidence might be found that reinstates collateral kin selection as a primary binding force. For the present, however, the ongoing shift to group-level selection forced by empirical evidence suggests that it might be profitable to undertake a similar new look at the wellsprings of social evolution in human beings and nonhuman vertebrates where, I believe, surprises also await us.'

7. R.D. Alexander, *The Biology of Moral Systems* (New York: Aldine de Gruyter, 1987).

8. G.S. Wilkinson, 'Reciprocal food sharing in the vampire bat', *Nature*, 308, 1984, pp. 181–4. See Ridley, *The Origins of Virtue*, pp. 62–3.

9. See Ridley, ibid., pp. 69–70.

10. Darwin noted in *The Descent of Man* (1871), 'A tribe including many members who, from possessing in high degree the spirit of patriotism, fidelity, obedience, courage and sympathy, were always ready to aid one another, and to sacrifice themselves for the

common good, would be victorious over most other tribes; and this would be natural selection.'

11. Ridley, *The Origins of Virtue*, p. 175.

12. See ibid., p. 193.

13. ibid., pp. 179–80. He notes that human altruism, or apparent altruism, is very deeply entrenched: 'all human beings share a fascinating taboo . . . the taboo against selfishness. Selfishness is almost the definition of vice. Murder, theft, rape and fraud are considered crimes of great importance because they are selfish and spiteful acts that are committed for the benefit of the actor and the detriment of the victim. In contrast, virtue is, almost by definition, the greater good of the group. Those virtues (such as thrift or abstinence) that are not directly altruistic in their motivation are few and obscure. The conspicuously virtuous things we all praise – co-operation, altruism, generosity, sympathy, kindness, selflessness – are all unambiguously concerned with the welfare of others. This is not some parochial Western tradition. It is a bias shared by the whole species' (p. 38).

14. Stephen Jay Gould, 'Evolution and the pleasures of pluralism', *New York Review of Books*, 44, 1997, pp. 47–52.

15. Richard Dawkins, *The Selfish Gene* (Oxford: Oxford University Press, 1976), p. 201.

16. Dawkins, *A Devil's Chaplain*, pp. 13, 15.

17. See Jeffrey P. Schloss, 'Love Creation's Final Law? Emerging Evolutionary Accounts of Altruism', in S. Post, L. Underwood, J. Schloss and W. Hurlbut (eds), *Altruism and Altruistic Love: Science, Philosophy, and Religion in Dialogue* (Oxford: Oxford University Press, 2002), pp. 212–42; Jeffrey P. Schloss, 'Hath Darwin Suffered a Prophet's Scorn? Evolutionary Theory and the Scandal of Unconditional Love', in Charles Harper (ed.), *Spiritual Information* (West Conshohocken, PA: Templeton Foundation Press, 2005), pp. 291–9; Jeffrey P. Schloss, 'Evolutionary Ethics and Christian Morality: Surveying the Issues', in Philip Clayton and Jeffrey Schloss (eds), *Evolution and Ethics: Human Morality in Biological and Religious Perspective* (Grand Rapids: Eerdmans, 2004), pp. 1–24.

18. Warren Brown summarises the view of the game theorist Robert Wright, and the effect of that view, as follows: 'Wright argues that the existence of non-zero [sumness] is evidence that evolution has an inevitable direction toward increasing complexity of organisms, necessarily resulting in complex, sentient and (in my words) relational creatures like humankind. According to the concept of non-zero, the progress of evolution has been influenced by a fundamental principle of the survival value of cooperative effort. This principle would make it inevitable that creatures would become more and more complex. This trajectory toward cooperation and complexity would necessarily result in complex relational creatures like humans. Once the neural/mental capacities of early humankind reaches a level to sustain culture, culture would itself be driven to increasing complexity by the same rules of nonzero-sumness. To put it theologically, God's intent to create humankind (ie creatures capable of personal relatedness and soulishness) was encoded in the universe within the universal law that survival benefits accrue from co-operation, and what is good for one is generally good for all. Although not promoting a theological position, Wright speculates that "this directionality provides at least some evidence that the evolutionary process is subordinate to a larger purpose – a 'higher' purpose, you might say"'; in 'Evolution, Cognitive Neuroscience and the Soul', in Miller (ed), *Perspectives on an Evolving Creation*, pp. 522–3.

19. S.L. Brown, R. Nesse, A.D. Vinokur and D.M. Smith, in *Psychological Science*, 14, 2003, pp. 320–7.

20. S.L. Brown and R.M. Brown, 'Selective Investment Theory: Recasting the Functional Significance of Close Relationships', *Psychological Inquiry*, 17:1, 2006, pp. 1–29.

21. It is not biologically inconceivable that what we do (for instance by doing good deeds) might in some way mould us physically in a way that confers a survival benefit. Parts of the cerebral cortex devoted in sighted people to vision are recruited in blind people for tactile processing. See, for instance, Norihiro Sadato, et al., 'Tactile discrimination activates the visual cortex of the recently blind naive to Braille: a functional MRI study in humans',

Neuroscience Letters, 359:1–2, 2004, pp. 49–52. Rates of Alzheimer's disease are significantly higher in illiterate people – see Alfredo Ardila and Maria Rosselli, 'Illiterates and cognition: the impact of education', in Barbara Uzzell, et al. (eds), *International Handbook of Cross-Cultural Neuropsychology* (London: Routledge, 2007). We can affect how we are wired, and how we are wired may affect the way we look to natural selection.

Chapter 5

1. Richard Dawkins, *The God Delusion* (London: Bantam Press, 2006).

2. ibid., p. 192.

3. Daniel Dennett, *Breaking the Spell: Religion as a Natural Phenomenon* (London: Penguin, 2007).

4. It is perhaps worth pointing out that everyone agrees that you need a pretty big brain to be religious. There is dispute about how big – about what sort of Theory of Mind you need. Robin Dunbar, for instance, contends that to have communal religion you need fifth order intentionality – the highest order of which humans are generally thought capable. In other words, you need the sort of brain that can follow a statement such as 'I intend that you believe that we want the spirits to be willing to intervene in the world in the way we want them to'. See 'Why are humans not just great apes?', in Charles Pasternak (ed), *What Makes Us Human?* (Oxford: Oneworld, 2007), p. 44.

5. See Justin Barrett, *Why Would Anyone Believe in God?* (Walnut Creek, CA, and Oxford: Altamira Press, 2004), pp. 31–44.

6. See ibid., p. 31.

7. Gould, 'Evolution and the pleasures of pluralism', p. 51.

8. Although they struggle to explain the distinctly anti-conformist strands in Judaism's and Christianity's radical prophetic tradition. It is hard to see Isaiah or Amos as yes-men, policing conformity to societal norms.

9. Jeffrey Schloss, *Naturalistic Explanations of Religion: Explaining or Explaining Away?* (Faraday Institute, 2007).

10. Ian Tattersall, *Becoming Human: Evolution and Human Uniqueness* (Oxford: Oxford University Press, 1998), pp. 1–3.

11. On one level I believe that the (immediate) answer lies in David Lewis-Williams's 'neuropsychological' explanation for Upper Palaeolithic cave art, which postulates that this art represents shamanic experiences while on trance-journeys to supposed other worlds. But this assertion begs a number of questions to which I return in *Wired for God?* (Hodder & Stoughton, forthcoming).

Chapter 6

1. Philadelphia: Presbyterian and Reformed Publishing, 1961.

2. The system of assigning numerical values to each letter in the Hebrew alphabet.

3. There is a third account of the creation of man in Genesis 5:1–2. We deal later with the significance of that. Other differences and relationships between Genesis 1 and 2 are asserted. It is contended by Conrad Hyers, for instance, that Genesis 1 (which sees too much water as a threat, humans as essentially royal, and is happy with civilisation and its fruits) is written from the perspective of an agricultural/urban people, whereas Genesis 2 – 3 (which sees the threat rather as dryness/barrenness, humans as servants in an oasis, and goodness as a simple life) is the pastoral/nomadic perspective. See 'Comparing Biblical and Scientific Maps of Origins', in Miller, *Perspectives on an Evolving Creation*, pp. 21–4.

4. Gen. 1:11–12.

5. Gen. 1:20–2.

6. Gen. 1:24–7.

7. Gen. 2:4–7.

8. Gen. 2:18–19.

9. Gen. 2:20–2.

10. Gen. 3:1 (added emphasis).

11. Gen. 3:14.

12. Gen. 3:14.

13. Gen. 4:14.

14. Gen. 4:15.

15. Gen. 4:16–17.

16. Rom. 5:12.

17. Exod. 15:6.

18. Other examples include: 'You stretched out your right hand, the earth swallowed them' (Exod. 15:12); 'The right hand of the LORD does valiantly; the right hand of the LORD is exalted (Ps. 118:15–16); 'your right hand shall hold me fast' (Ps. 139:10); 'His right hand and his holy arm have gained him victory' (Ps. 98:1); 'The LORD has sworn by his right hand and by his mighty arm' (Isa. 62:8); 'My hand laid the foundation of the earth, and my right hand spread out the heavens' (Isa. 48:13). See also, if the point has not already been laboured to death, Pss. 21:8; 44:3; 74:11; 89:13; 118:16; 138:7.

19. Ps. 19:4–5.

20. Gen. 1:6–8.

21. See Gen. 1:16.

22. See Gen 1:1–3.

23. See Gen. 1:3–19.

24. The earliest theologians did not struggle with such questions. See, for instance, the quotation from Origen at the head of this chapter.

25. Ps. 93:1 says that '[the Lord] has established the world; it shall never be moved'.

26. John Calvin, *Commentaries on the First Book of Moses, called Genesis*, trans. John King (Grand Rapids: Eerdmans, 1948), 1:79.

27. ibid., 1:84.

28. Gen. 1:1.

29. It is made explicit in Deut. 4:15–19.

30. Gen. 1:14–18. The plants were created on day three: Gen. 1:11–12.

31. Gen. 1:3–4.

32. See Gen. 1:14–18.

33. Gen. 1:26–8.

34. Gen. 1:6–8.

35. See Leon Kass, *The Beginning of Wisdom: Reading Genesis* (Chicago: University of Chicago Press, 2006). There may be other numerological connotations to the seven days. Numerologically,

7 implies completeness, wholeness and totality. It is also a combination of 3 and 4. Conrad Heyers suggests that the '3' here is a reference to the three vertical zones of the cosmos (heaven, earth and the underworld floating on the cosmic ocean), and that the '4' refers to the horizontal dimensions of the cosmos (the four directions, the four corners of the earth, the four quarters). And 3 x 4 = 12 – a number that resonates throughout the Bible. See Hyers, 'Comparing Biblical and Scientific Maps of Origins', pp. 24–6.

36. Gen. 2:4.

37. Ps. 104:26.

38. The degree of delegation is profound and alarming. Philip Hefner speaks of human beings as 'created co-creators'; cited in John Polkinghorne, 'Kenotic Creation and Divine Creation', in John Polkinghorne (ed.), *The Work of Love: Creation as Kenosis* (Grand Rapids, Michigan: Eerdmans, 2001), p. 95.

39. Gen. 1:1.

40. See Claus Westermann, *Genesis 1 – 11: A Commentary* (London: SPCK, 1984), pp. 95–8.

41. e.g. in Isa. 41:20.

42. Gen. 1:1–2.

43. Gen. 1:6–7.

44. Gen. 1:9.

45. Gen. 1:11.

46. Gen. 1:20.

47. Gen. 1:24.

48. Gen. 1:27 – although Genesis does say that although they were 'brought forth', God 'created' or 'made' the animals: see Gen. 1:21 and 1:25. He is not said to have 'created' the plants. They have to be content with having been 'brought forth': see Gen. 1:11–12.

49. Gen. 2:7.

50. Gen. 2:19.

51. See Westermann, *Genesis 1 – 11*, p. 125. Cf. Isa. 61:11; Hag. 1:11; Num. 17:23; Ps. 104:14.

52. Gen. 2:5, see Kass, *The Beginning of Wisdom*, p. 58.

53. The order in the second creation story is, of course, radically different.

54. Gen. 1:11–12.

55. Gen. 1:20–1.

56. Gen. 1:24–5.

57. e.g. Gen. 6:20; 7:14; Lev. 11:14, 22, 29; Deut. 14:13–15, 18. For further discussion, see Westermann, *Genesis 1 – 11*, p. 126, and Gordon Wenham, *Genesis: Word Biblical Commentary* (Waco, Texas: Word Books, 1987), p. 21. Westermann observes that the word is used in two contexts in the Old Testament: in the creation narrative, and in the context of the distinction between clean and unclean animals. (There is a reference in Ezek. 47:10 which has no recognisable context, and may be a late addition.) Westermann comments: 'Even if its use is different in these two groups of texts, its general sense remains the same. Occasionally it is used in the context of knowledge. The wise or the clever man can distinguish and enumerate the different kind of things. In the context of [the Priestly source's] careful distinction of the species of plants and animals, one can speak of a scientific interest, provided one distinguishes it from our idea of "science". This distinction is not made for its own sake, out of some need to classify in order to take proper possession of the object, though this may have had some weight with [the Priestly source]. The function of the classification of the plants and animals lies in its significance for people. This is a reflection of the earlier stage when the creation of each lot of plants and animals was the subject of a creation story in itself and looked to the particular needs of humanity. The distinction between the two major groups [of vegetation], "plants" and "trees" is made primarily from the point of view of their meaning for people and for the animals . . . as is the distinction between the various species of seeds and fruits. Clearly then, the way in which this distinction is formulated is the result of careful thought; one can see the transition to theoretical reflection on the basis of the distinctions. This is shown by a comparison with Exodus 10:15 . . . where the same division into "plants" and "fruit-trees" occurs, but without the further interest shown in Genesis 1.'

58. Gen. 1:20.

59. Gen. 1:24.

60. See Kass, *The Beginning of Wisdom*, p. 48.

61. The plague of frogs – see Exod. 8:1–15.

62. For more detailed discussion of this issue, see Kass, *The Beginning of Wisdom*, pp. 49–50.

63. Gen. 1:3.

64. Gen. 1:11–12.

65. Gen. 1:20.

66. Gen. 1:21.

67. See Kass, *The Beginning of Wisdom*, pp. 49–51.

68. Gen. 1:4.

69. Gen. 1:5.

70. George Caird, *Principalities and Powers* (Oxford: Clarendon Press, 1956), p. 59; cited in Michael Lloyd, 'Are Animals Fallen?', in Andrew Linzey and Dorothy Yamamoto (eds), *Animals on the Agenda* (London: SPCK, 1998), pp. 155–6.

71. Gen. 1:31.

72. Ps. 19:1.

73. Westermann, *Genesis 1 – 11*, pp. 166–7.

74. Gen. 1:29.

75. Gen. 1:30.

76. Gen. 1:30.

77. See, for instance, Bernhard W. Anderson, *From Creation to New Creation: Old Testament Perspectives* (Philadelphia: Fortress, 1994), p. 34: 'Creation is basically an eschatological doctrine in the sense that it has a future horizon . . . The opening words of Genesis "In the beginning God . . ." correspond to the prophetic expectation "in the end God".' Cited in Miller, *Perspectives on an Evolving Creation*, p. 416. See generally Jeffrey Schloss, 'From Evolution to Eschatology', in Ted Peters, Robert J. Russell and Michael Welker (eds), *Resurrection: Theological and Scientific Assessments* (Grand Rapids: Eerdmans, 2002), pp. 56–85.

78. Isa. 11:6–9.

79. See Gen. 6:21: 'Also take with you [in the ark] every kind of food

that is eaten, and store it up; and it shall serve as food for you and for them.'

80. Gen. 8:20.
81. Gen. 6:11–12.
82. Gen. 9:1–4.
83. Gen. 9:1, 7.
84. Gen. 1:28.

Chapter 7

1. N.K. Smith (ed.) (Indianapolis: Bubbs-Merrill, 1947), p. 211.
2. Carl Gustav Boberg, 1885, trans. Stuart Hine.
3. 'Wonderful World', from *Something Fischy*, Stephen Fischbacher.
4. Letter to Hooker, 13 July 1856; www.darwinproject.ac.uk, Letter no. 1924.
5. Polkinghorne, 'Kenotic creation and divine action', in Polkinghorne (ed.), *The Work of Love*, p. 93.
6. G.C. Williams, *Plan and Purpose in Nature* (New York: Basic Books, 1996), p. 157, cited in Dawkins, *A Devil's Chaplain*, p. 11.
7. David L. Hull, 'God of the Galapagos', *Nature*, 352, 1992, pp. 485–6, cited in Christopher Southgate, *The Groaning of Creation* (Louisville: Westminster John Knox Press, 2008), p. 7.
8. C.S. Lewis, *A Grief Observed* (London: Faber & Faber, 1961; first published under the pseudonym of N.W. Clerk).
9. C.S. Lewis, *The Problem of Pain* (London: Geoffrey Bles, 1940, reprinted Fontana Books, 1972), p. 4. All subsequent references are to the Fontana edition.
10. Pascal, *Pensees* IV, 242–3, cited in Lewis, ibid., p. 1.
11. v. 21.
12. Job 39:14–15.
13. Isa. 30:30–3.
14. Augustine, *City of God*, 1:20, cited in Linzey and Yamamoto, *Animals on the Agenda*, p. xiii.
15. Aquinas, *Summa contra Gentiles*, trans. English Dominican Fathers, Benzger Brothers, 1928, Third Book, Part II, chapter cxii, cited in Linzey and Yamamoto, ibid., p. xiii. See generally Gillian

Clark, 'The Fathers and the Animals: The Rule of Reason?', in Linzey and Yamamoto, ibid., pp. 67–79.

16. Joseph Rickaby, *Moral Philosophy: Ethics, Deontology and Natural Law* (London: Longmans, Green and Co., 1918), cited in Linzey and Yamamoto, ibid., p. 66.

17. Gen. 2:15 is usually translated along the lines of, 'The LORD God took the man and put him in the garden of Eden to till it and keep it . . .' The Hebrew word 'to till' here is *avad*, and can also be rendered 'to serve'. See Kass, *The Beginning of Wisdom*, p. 58.

18. See too Exod. 23:5, 12; Lev. 22:24; Num. 20:8; 22:32; Deut. 5:14; 20:19; 22:4; 25:4.

19. I am using 'suffering' here in a sense that will become clear. In the context of physical suffering, it essentially amounts to something like: 'Discharge of pain receptors, plus an acknowledgement that this discharge represents some threat to the bodily or mental or spiritual integrity of the suffering creature.'

20. Lewis, *The Problem of Pain*, pp. 119–20.

21. ibid., p. 121.

22. See, for instance, Conway Morris, *Life's Solution*, pp. 242–64.

23. Fyodor Dostoevsky, *The Brothers Karamazov*, Book V, Chapter iv, trans. Constance Garnett, 1912.

24. ibid.

25. Thus Stephen Hawking (for instance) wrote, 'These [physical] laws may have originally been decreed by God, but it appears that he has since left the universe to evolve according to them and does not now intervene in it'; *A Brief History of Time* (New York: Bantam Books, 1988), p. 122.

26. Ps. 104:10–14, 16–18, 25–30; see too Ps. 145:15–16. The provision is said to warrant the praise of his creatures: e.g. Ps. 148 :1–10; Rev. 5:11–13.

27. Ps. 145:9.

28. Matt. 6:26, 28–9; cf. Luke 12:24–7.

29. Matt. 10:29–31; cf. Luke 12:6–7.

30. Mark 1:13.

31. Matt. 14:2; Luke 22:7.

32. Luke 5:1–9; John 21:4–11.
33. John 21:9, 13.
34. Matt. 8:28–32; Mark 5:1–13; Luke 8:26–33.

Chapter 8

1. London: Longmans, Green and Co., 1927, pp. 522–3, cited in Lloyd, 'Are Animals Fallen?', p. 157.
2. See K.A. Kitchen, *On the Reliability of the Old Testament* (Grand Rapids, Michigan: Eerdmans, 2003), p. 429. He notes that four 'head' rivers come together to form the single stream that entered the garden. These were the Pishon, Gishon, Tigris and Euphrates. Today, the Tigris and Euphrates join up in southern Iraq to form the Shatt al-Arab which enters the Gulf. But it was not so in antiquity. Accordingly, he says, the 'heads' of these two must have been their sources – their headwaters – and similarly for the Gishon and the Pishon. Both the Tigris and the Euphrates rise in the mountains of eastern Anatolia. The biblical 'Kush' is probably Kashshur – the land of the Kassites in western Iran. The Gishon rose there, although its identification is uncertain. The real difficulty relates to the Pishon. Kitchen suggests that it may be a long-dried river that rose in western Arabia and flowed east and north-east towards the head of the Gulf, via Kuwait. Such a river flowed to at least 2500–2200 BC, but by the time that Genesis was committed to papyrus, it would have been a folk memory.
3. Gen. 2:9.
4. See Kass, *The Beginning of Wisdom*, p. 63.
5. Gen. 2:15.
6. Gen. 2:16–17.
7. Gen. 3:12–13.
8. Gen. 3:14–19.
9. This is not, of course, the only way of reading the text. Michael Lloyd, for instance, would maintain that the tree of life indicates that human beings are not *intrinsically* immortal, but are dependent for their immortality (which was always God's intention for them) on something external – namely God's moment-by-moment

sustenance. While they were in the garden, and in a state of obedience, they had constant access to that moment-by-moment divine maintenance. Since their expulsion, they have no such access and, rather as a car left unmaintained falls slowly to pieces, decay begins. It follows from this view that had they been obedient, they would have had de facto immortality. He would draw support from this view from the Bible's general abhorrence for physical death, exemplified by the laws of ritual impurity associated with contact with a corpse, by Jesus' tears over Lazarus, and by the glorious end, in which access to the tree of life is restored and death passes away. This view is immensely attractive in many ways, but (a) I cannot square it exegetically with the passage; and (b) I cannot square it archaeologically with what we see in the soil of East Africa and the Levant. Of which much more in chapter 9.

10. Gen. 3:22.
11. Gen. 3:23–4.
12. Gen. 3:19.
13. See p. 122.
14. Gen. 3:15.
15. Gen. 3:16.
16. Gen. 3:17.
17. Gen. 3:17–19.
18. Unless Ps. 51:5 is hinting at it.
19. See the discussion in Linzey and Yamamoto, *Animals on the Agenda*, pp. 26–8.
20. AD 354–430.
21. Rom. 5:12 (emphasis added).
22. But see the contrary view of Anthony Thiselton: '*paraptoma* ... denotes an offense or a habit of wrongdoing'; *The Hermeneutics of Doctrine* (Grand Rapids: Eerdmans, 2007), p. 269.
23. Rom. 5:21.
24. See Rom. 5:16, 18.
25. Douglas Moo, *The Epistle to the Romans* (Grand Rapids, Michigan: Eerdmans, 1996), p. 320.
26. Lewis, *The Problem of Pain*, pp. 74–6.

27. 1 Cor. 15:21–2.

28. 1 Cor. 15:47–51.

29. C.S. Lewis, *Reflections on the Psalms* (London: Geoffrey Bles, 1958).

30. Rom. 1:20.

31. Rom. 8:19–22.

32. Lewis, *The Problem of Pain*, p. 121.

33. Note Jesus' comment in Luke 13:1–5: 'At that very time there were some present who told him about the Galileans whose blood Pilate had mingled with their sacrifices. He asked them: "Do you think that because these Galileans suffered in this way they were worse sinners than all other Galileans? No, I tell you; but unless you repent, you will all perish as they did. Or those eighteen who were killed when the tower of Siloam fell on them – do you think that they were worse offenders than all the others living in Jerusalem? No, I tell you; but unless you repent, you will all perish just as they did."'

34. The issue is well discussed in Lewis, *The Problem of Pain*, chapter 2, 'Divine Omnipotence'.

35. See Lloyd, 'Are Animals Fallen?', pp. 150–1.

36. Ibid., pp. 151–5.

37. See the discussion at pp. 129–31.

38. Gen. 1:11.

39. Gen. 1:20.

40. Gen. 1:24.

41. See the discussion at pp. 132–4.

42. Thomas E. Hosinksi, 'How does God's providential care extend to animals?', in Linzey and Yamamoto, *Animals on the Agenda*, pp. 140–1. See too Jürgen Moltmann, 'God's kenosis in the creation and consummation of the world', in Polkinghorne, *The Work of Love*, pp. 150–1: 'the God who in patience bears and endures the history of nature and human beings, allows time and gives time, and in so doing makes possible ever-new possibilities, which are either realised or not realised, and can be used for further development but also for annihilation.'

43. The same idea is put well by Arthur Peacocke: 'there are inherent

constraints on how even an omnipotent Creator could bring about the existence of a law-like creation that is to be a cosmos, not a chaos, and thus an arena for the free action of self-conscious, reproducing, complex entities and for the coming to be of the fecund variety of living organisms whose existence the Creator delights in'; 'The Cost of New Life', in Polkinghorne, ibid., p. 37.

44. Process thinkers like Arthur Peacocke (who is also one of the main architects of kenotic theories) seem to suggest that God has no such power: 'Instead of being daunted by the role of chance in genetic mutation as being the manifestation of irrationality in the universe, it would be more consistent with the observations to assert that the full gamut of the possibilities of living matter could be explored only through the agency of the rapid and frequent randomisation which is possible at the molecular level of the DNA'; *Creation and the World of Science* (Oxford: Clarendon Press, 1979), p. 94.

45. Peacocke, 'The Cost of New Life', p. 34.

46. Discussed in more detail by Jay B. McDaniel, 'Can animal suffering be reconciled with belief in an all-loving God?', in Linzey and Yamamoto, *Animals on the Agenda*, pp. 160–70.

47. Phil. 2:6–8.

48. Phil. 2:9.

49. Cf. Moltmann, 'God's kenosis in the creation and consummation of the world', p. 149.

50. At the very start of *The Problem of Pain*, C.S. Lewis cites George Macdonald (*Unspoken Sermons*, First Series): 'The Son of God suffered unto the death, not that men might not suffer, but that their sufferings might be like His.' Does a similar thought work for the sufferings of non-human animals?

51. Holmes Rolston III, for instance, believes that 'Suffering is a key to the whole, not intrinsically, not as an end in itself, but as a transformative principle, transvalued into its opposite'; *Science and Religion: A Critical Survey* (New York: Random House, 1987), cited in Peacocke, 'The Cost of New Life', p. 31.

52. Exemplified in their essays in Polkinghorne, *The Work of Love*:

Holmes Rolston III, 'Kenosis and Nature', pp. 43–65; Peacocke, 'The Cost of New Life', pp. 21–42.

53. There tends, too, to be a lot of dubiously relevant citation of John 12:24: 'Unless a grain of wheat falls into the earth and dies, it remains just a single grain; but if it dies, it bears much fruit.'

54. See, for instance, John Munday, 'Animal Pain: Beyond the Threshold?', in Miller, *Perspectives on an Evolving Creation*, p. 439.

55. David Livingstone, *Livingstone's Africa*, cited in M.A. Corey, *Back to Darwin: The Scientific Case for Deistic Education* (Lanham, MD: University Press of America, 1994), p. 373.

56. e.g. Whitehead, Hartshorne and the other architects of process theodicy.

57. *The Ideas of the Fall and of Original Sin*, p. 513, cited in Lloyd, 'Are Animals Fallen?', p. 157.

58. Other suggestions in Jewish thought about how evil entered the world included Satan (see Wisdom of Solomon 2:24: 'God created man for incorruption . . . but through the devil's envy death entered the world, and those who belong to his party experience it'), Eve (Sirach 25:24: 'From a woman sin had its beginning, and because of her we all die'; see too *Adam and Eve* 44; Apocalypse of Moses 14:32), and the 'evil heart' (4 Ezra 4:30).

59. Lewis, *The Problem of Pain*, pp. 122–3.

60. Rev. 13:8 (NIV).

61. John 19:30.

62. Gen. 2:2.

63. Rev. 22:2.

64. Rev. 22:3.

65. Rev. 21:4. See too the perspective in Job 42:10–17 – the flavour of it is in v. 10. After all Job's trials, 'the LORD restored the fortunes of Job . . . and the LORD gave Job twice as much as he had before'.

66. See N.T. Wright, *Surprised by Hope* (London: SPCK, 2008).

67. Luke 23:43.

68. See Linzey and Yamamoto, *Animals on the Agenda*, p. xvi; also p. xviii: 'the incarnation as God's love affair with the flesh – not

only the flesh of humankind, but all embodied, sentient creatures'. But why just sentient ones?

69. See Rev. 21:2; also 19:7–9.
70. For the theme of the new heaven and the new earth, see Rev. 21:1;
2 Peter 3:13.
71. This is put well by Keith Ward: 'this cosmos is the soil in which
the seeds of eternal life are sown. Its future will be unlike its
present, and yet causally related to it – a consummation and not
a cancellation of history'; 'Cosmos and Kenosis', in Polkinghorne,
The Work of Love, p. 165.
72. Rev. 22:20.
73. Col. 1:20.
74. *The Brothers Karamazov*, Book V, Chapter IV.

Chapter 9

1. Published 1734.
2. For a splendid account of the discovery, see Donald Johanson and
Maitland Edey, *Lucy: The Beginnings of Humankind* (London:
Penguin, 1990), pp. 17–22.
3. The trigger for bipedalism is much discussed, but climate change
is likely to be a factor. Before the devastation of modern times,
climate change dealt three massive blows to African forests –
5–6 million years ago, 2.5 million years ago and 1.8 million years
ago. Each resulted in an increased proportion of savannah and
forest-edge habitats. Open-country antelopes increased; forest
browsers decreased. And each of these times coincided with a
significant step in hominid evolution. In open country, long legs
are good as viewing posts: you can see further. They are also
good for walking long distances. And the shorter legs useful for
swinging from trees are less useful. Hominids gradually weaned
themselves further and further away from the forests. The first
hominid that we know was entirely free from forest edges – a
true savannah dweller – was the 'Turkana Boy' – a nine-year-old
boy from the west side of Lake Turkana. His skeleton is almost
complete. Only his hands and feet are missing. He dates from

about 1.6 million years ago. He has an entirely modern *body* form, but his skull and teeth are different from other hominids found in the Turkana region that are undoubtedly *Homo*. Debate continues to rage as to how the Turkana Boy fits into the human story. For further discussion, see Tattersall, *The Monkey in the Mirror*, pp. 79–106.

4. There are, as ever, some caveats to insert. Tattersall and Schwartz summarise the position as follows: 'Burial in the simple Neanderthal style . . . falls short of furnishing us with convincing proof of symbolic activity among these extinct hominids. Is there anything else in the record bequeathed us by the Neanderthals that might suggest such a thing? Well, actually, rather little. That the Neanderthals had curiosity and some form of aesthetic sense is suggested by the finding at one site of an occasional fossil imported from another. There are, however, few convincing instances of actual symbolic productions . . . [Such evidence as there is] only serve[s] to emphasize the rarity of such behaviours amongst the Neanderthals: something that contrasts dramatically with the torrential outpouring of symbolic artefacts by the early moderns who succeeded the Neanderthals in Europe. The evidence is poor that the shared cultural expressions of the Neanderthals were routinely or even ever symbolically mediated. There is one possible exception [the Chatelperronian stone tool industry in western France and adjacent regions. The interpretation of the Chatelperronian sites is notoriously controversial]. But it remains true that the only good association of symbolic objects with Neanderthals comes in a period during which contact of some kind between [Neanderthals] and the arriving moderns was inevitable'; Ian Tattersall and Jeffrey Schwartz, *Extinct Humans* (Boulder, Colorado: Westview Press, 2000), pp. 217–18.

5. ibid., pp. 215–16.

6. 'Mitochondrial Eve' – the matrilineal most recent common ancestor of all current living humans, is thought to have lived about a hundred and forty thousand years ago in East Africa.

7. Some suggest, however, that Neanderthals expanded south to fill

the gap left by the departure of these anatomically modern *Homo sapiens*.

8. In Europe, Upper Palaeolithic culture has generally been called Cro-Magnon culture. The term is increasingly falling out of vogue.

9. Some suggest that there was no dramatic explosion at all, and that the appearance of an explosion is an artefact of the archaeological record. They point out that the sort of artefacts one would expect in the Middle Palaeolithic (three hundred thousand to fifty thousand years ago), and which could have indicated symbolic thought, would have been made from perishable materials such as wood, and would therefore not have survived. They posit instead a gradual emergence of symbolic behaviour. It has been (highly controversially) suggested, based on findings from the Atapuerca site in Spain, that *Homo heidelbergensis*, in the Lower Palaeolithic, may have ritually buried his dead. One has to search far and wide, though, for scholarly support for any sort of religion or real symbolism before the Middle Palaeolithic. Such suggestions for the Middle Palaeolithic are more common. In the Tsodilo Hills of the Kalahari, for instance, there is evidence, from about seventy thousand years ago, of a python cult centred on a giant, snake-shaped rock. Red ochre, which we met at Qafzeh, is found increasingly from late Middle Palaeolithic African sites (a hundred to fifty thousand years ago), and again might be associated with ritual of some kind. Some opponents of the 'explosion' theory rely on the intrinsic improbability of a sudden event. Oppenheimer is a good example: 'Language is the best candidate driver of brain size . . . it is much more likely that we were already communicating usefully and deliberately 2.5 million years ago, and that this drove our brain growth, than that our brains grew until some threshold size was reached and we miraculously discovered we could talk . . . [O]f all the mental and practical skills that philosophers, biologists and theologians have put forward as qualitative differences between modern humans and chimps, the only one that remains is human speech. Clearly, there is a great quantitative difference in intellectual ability, but human intellect did not suddenly flower 35,000 years ago in the European Upper

Palaeolithic – it had been evolving over the previous 4 million years. For the past 2 million years humans have been improving on the walking-ape model by using their brains, but they may have been aided in this by speech-driven co-evolution in brain size'; 'Our Ancestors and the Weather', in Pasternak, *What Makes Us Human?*, pp. 107–11.

10. Richard G. Klein describes the appearance of these people as 'the most dramatic behavioural shift that archaeologists will ever detect'; 'Archaeology of Modern Human Origins', *Evolutionary Anthropology*, 1:1, 1992, p. 5, cited in James P. Hurd, 'Hominids in the Garden', in Miller, *Perspectives on an Evolving Creation*, p. 219.

11. See the discussion in Tattersall and Schwartz, *Extinct Humans*, pp. 240–1.

12. e.g. Susan Blackmore, 'Imitation makes us human', in Pasternak, *What Makes Us Human?*, p. 14: 'What makes us human? In the beginning it was imitation and the appearance of memes. Now it is the way we work as meme machines, living in the culture that the memes have used us to build.' Note 'used'. She explains, 'Central to the idea of memes is that because they are replicators, evolution happens for the benefit of the memes themselves, rather than for their carriers or for anything else'; p. 3.

13. e.g. Richard Harries, 'Half ape, half angel?', in Pasternak, ibid., pp. 71–81.

14. e.g. Michael Corballis and Thomas Suddendorff, 'Memory, time and language', in Pasternak, ibid., pp. 17–36.

15. Tattersall, *The Monkey in the Mirror*, p. 184.

16. ibid., p. 152.

17. Gen. 1:21 (the water creatures and the birds); Gen. 1:25 (the terrestrial animals).

18. Gen. 1:27.

19. Gen. 1:28.

20. Gen. 1:22.

21. See the discussion in chapter 6.

22. Despite the apparent fact, discussed earlier, that the light may have been in some sort of early rebellion against the creator's

edit. That rebellion is probably better seen as a refusal of something dwelling *within* the created order to bow the knee, rather than of the inanimate created things themselves. The thing dwelling within is rather like a malleable skeleton, distinct from the thing it supports. The posture of the created thing is determined to some extent by the posture of that skeleton. If the skeleton is bent, so will the thing be. Thus the light is not quite what it should be because it is moulded to some extent to the twisted shape of that skeleton.

23. Kass, *The Beginning of Wisdom*, p. 39.
24. Gen. 1:28.
25. Gen. 1:28.
26. Gen. 1:28.
27. Gen. 1:15.
28. See Gen. 2:4–7.
29. C.S. Lewis's speculations about the moral consciousness of primordial man are probably as near as anyone will ever get: 'The self-surrender which [primeval man] practised before the Fall meant no struggle but only the delicious overcoming of an infinitesimal self-adherence which delighted to be overcome – of which we see a dim analogy in the rapturous mutual self-surrender of lovers even now. He had therefore, no *temptation* (in our sense) to choose the self – no passion or inclination obstinately inclining that way – nothing but the bare fact that the self was *him*self. Up to that moment [the fall] the human spirit had been in full control of the human organism. It doubtless expected that it would retain this control when it ceased to obey God. But its authority over the organism was a delegated authority which it lost when it ceased to be God's delegate'; *The Problem of Pain*, p. 69.
30. Gen. 2:16.
31. Gen. 2:17.
32. Kass, *The Beginning of Wisdom*, p. 64.
33. Gen. 2:18.
34. See Kass, *The Beginning of Wisdom*, pp. 72–3.
35. Gen. 2:18.
36. Gen. 2:19.

37. See Kass, *The Beginning of Wisdom*, pp. 73–4.

38. Gen. 2:20.

39. Gen. 2:21: 'So the LORD God caused a deep sleep to fall upon the man, and he slept; then he took one of his ribs and closed up its place with flesh.'

40. Gen. 2:19–20.

41. Gen. 2:23.

42. Gen. 2:25.

43. Gen. 3:1.

44. Gen. 3:1.

45. Gen. 3:2–3.

46. Gen. 2:9.

47. Gen. 2:17.

48. Gen. 3:4–5.

49. Gen. 3:6.

50. Gen. 3:7.

51. Gen. 3:12.

52. Gen. 3:13.

53. Gen. 3:11.

54. Gen. 3:12.

55. See pp. 159–68.

56. Gen. 3:17–19: 'cursed is the ground because of you; in toil you shall eat of it all the days of your life; thorns and thistles it shall bring forth for you ... By the sweat of your face you shall eat bread.'

57. Gen. 3:16: 'I will greatly increase your pangs in childbearing; in pain you shall bring forth children, yet your desire shall be for your husband.'

58. Gen. 3:7.

59. Gen. 3:22.

60. Eric Mascall wrote a poem about a discussion on the fall: 'We started with an Anglican of modernistic bent / Who argued that the Fall was not a Fall but an Ascent; / And what our jaundiced forefathers interpreted as vice, / Were harmless relics of the ape – and therefore rather nice' (courtesy of Michael Lloyd). That is not my view. I think that there is nothing nice about the fall at all.

61. Gen. 5:5.
62. See Gen. 4:1; 5:3–5.
63. Kass, *The Beginning of Wisdom*, p. 54. But I am no Pelagianist. I am not implying here that we all start off where Adam left off.
64. Gen. 3:22–3.
65. See John 3:3.
66. Matt. 18:3; cf. Luke 18:15–16; Matt. 19:14.
67. See Matt. 5:5.
68. Matt. 11:25.
69. See p. 115.
70. Gen. 4:1–16.
71. Gen. 4:21.
72. Gen. 4:22.
73. It is apparently not the 'breath of life' that God breathes into man's nostrils in Gen. 2:7, since the same expression is used of non-human animals in Gen. 1:30: 'And to every beast of the earth, and to every bird of the air, and to everything that creeps on the earth, *everything that has the breath of life*, I have given every green plant for food.'
74. Lewis, *The Problem of Pain*, p. 67.

Chapter 10

1. Conway Morris sets out in *Life's Solution* the facts about evolution that he thinks are congruent with a creation: '(1) its underlying simplicity, relying on a handful of building blocks; (2) the existence of an immense universe of possibilities, but a way of navigating to that minutest of fractions which actually work; (3) the sensitivity of the process and the product, whereby nearly all alternatives are disastrously maladaptive; (4) the inherency of life, whereby complexity emerges as much by the rearrangement and co-option of pre-existing building blocks as against relying on novelties per se; (5) the exuberance of biological diversity, but the ubiquity of evolutionary convergence; (6) the inevitability of the emergence of sentience, and the likelihood that among animals it is far more prevalent than we are willing to admit'; p. 329.

2. Kurt Wise, in Ashton, *In Six Days* (1999), cited in Dawkins, *The God Delusion*, p. 285.
3. The accommodation with Darwinism routinely adopted was worked out in the nineteenth century and has barely changed. Archbishop Temple wrote in 1885, 'What is touched by [evolution] is not the evidence of design but the mode in which the design was executed ... In the one case the Creator made the animals at once such as they are now; in the other case he impressed on matter ... such inherent powers that in the ordinary course of time living creatures such as the present were developed ... He did not make things, we may say; no, but he made things make themselves'; *The Relations between Religion and Science* (London: Macmillan, 1885), p. 114.
4. Although it can convincingly be inferred.

Index

Numerals in **bold** refer to illustrations; numerals in *italics* refer to notes

Index